CALEND
CONSTE
OF THE ANCIENT WORLD

CALENDARS AND CONSTELLATIONS OF THE ANCIENT WORLD

EMMELINE PLUNKET

SENATE

Calendars & Constellations of the Ancient World

First published in 1903 as *Ancient Calendars and Constellations* by John Murray, London.

This edition first published in 1997 by Senate, an imprint of Random House UK Ltd, Random House, 20 Vauxhall Bridge Road, London SW1V 2SA

ISBN 1 85958 488 8

Printed and bound in Guernsey by The Guernsey Press Co. Ltd

CONTENTS

PART I

PART II

ANCIENT CALENDARS AND CONSTELLATIONS

PART I

I

THE ACCADIAN CALENDAR

[Reprinted from the *Proceedings of the Society of Biblical Archæology, January* 1892]

Epping and Strassmaier, in their book *Astronomisches aus Babylon*, have lately translated three small documents, originally inscribed on clay tablets in the second century B.C. From these tablets, we learn that the Babylonians of the above date possessed a very advanced knowledge of the science of astronomy. Into the question of the extent of that knowledge we need not here enter further than to say that it enabled the Babylonian astronomers to draw up almanacs for the ensuing year; almanacs in which the eclipses of the sun and moon, and the times of the new and full moon, were accurately noted, as also the positions of the planets throughout the year. These positions were indicated by the nearness of the planet in question to some star in the vicinity of the ecliptic, and the ecliptic was portioned off into twelve groups, coinciding very closely in position and extent with the twelve divisions of the Zodiac as we now know them.

As to the calendar or mode of reckoning the year, we find that the order and names of the twelve months were as follows: Nisannu (or Nisan), Airu, Simannu, Dûzu, Abu, Ulûlu, Tischritu, Arah-samna, Kislimu, Tebitu, Šabâtu, Adaru.

Of these months Ulûlu and Adaru could be doubled as Ulûlu Sami (the second Elul), and Adaru Arki (the last Adar). The Babylonian years were soli-lunar: that is to say, the year of twelve lunar months, containing three hundred and fifty-four days, was bound to the solar year of three hundred and sixty-five days by intercalating, as occasion required, a thirteenth month.

Out of every eleven years there were seven with twelve months, and four with thirteen months. The first day of the year being, like some of our church festivals, dependent on the time of the new moon, was "moveable" (*schwankende*). The year, according to the tablets before Epping and Strassmaier, "*began with Nisan, hence in the spring.*"[1]

This is a sketch of the Babylonian calendar in the second century B.C., as drawn from the work of the two learned Germans above-named.

Now we find in the British Museum a great number of trade documents which, according to the Catalogue, "cover a period of over two thousand years." There are "tablets of the time of Rim-sin, Ḫammurabi, and Samsu-iluna; tablets of the time of the Assyrian supremacy, of the time of the native kings, and of the time

[1] "Was den Anfang des Jahres betrifft, so haben wir schon gezeigt, das die seleucidische Aera, wie sie in unseren drei Tafeln vorliegt, ihre Jahre mit dem Nisan, also im Frühjahr begann." (Epping and Strassmaier, *Astronomisches aus Babylon*, p. 181).

of the Persian supremacy; tablets of the times of the Seleucidæ, and the Arsacidæ."[1]

These documents are all dated in such and such a month of such and such a year of some king's reign; the months are the same (at first under their earlier Accadian names[2]) as those we

[1] See *Guide to the Nimroud Central Saloon*, B.M., 1886. The dates of the rulers mentioned are as follows:—

Rim-sin, about 2,300 B.C.

Ḫammurabi, about 2,200 B.C.

Samsu-iluna, about 2,100 B.C.

Assyrian supremacy from about 1275 to 609 B.C.

The latest tablet in the collection is dated, according to the Catalogue, 93 B.C.

[2] ASSYRIAN. ACCADIAN MONTH NAMES, AND TRANSLATIONS.

1. Ni'sannu, ...	*Sara* (or *Bar*) *zig-gar* ("the sacrifice of righteousness").
2. Airu, ...	*Khar-sidi* ("the propitious bull").
3. 'Sivanu, *or* Tsivan, .	*Mun-ga* ("of bricks"), and *Kas* ("the twins").
4. Duzu, ...	*Su kul-na* ("seizer of seed").
5. Abu, ...	*Ab ab-gar* ("fire that makes fire").
6. Ululu, ...	*Ki Gingir-na* ("the errand of Istar").
7. Tasritu, ...	*Tul-cu* ("the holy altar").
8. Arahk-samna ("the 8th month"), . .	*Apin-am-a* ("the bull-like founder?").
9. Cisilivu, *or* Cuzallu, .	*Gan ganna* ("the very cloudy").
10. Dharbitu, ...	*Abba uddu* ("the father of light").
11. Sabahu, ...	*As a-an* ("abundance of rain").
12. Addaru, ...	*Se-ki-sil* ("sowing of seed").
13. Arakh-makru ("the incidental month"),	*Se-dir* ("dark [month] of sowing").

—*Records of the Past*, vol. i. p. 166.

find in the almanacs translated by Epping and Strassmaier, and we meet in them, and in other historical inscriptions, with the intercalary months, the second Elul, and the second Adar. It would seem, then, that it was the same calendar, worked in the same way, that held its place through these two thousand years.[1]

[1] As evidence of the antiquity of a fixed calendrical method of counting the year, and of a method closely resembling, if not identical with, that used in the latest periods of Babylonian history, the importance and trustworthiness of these documents can scarcely be over-rated. They were inscribed on soft clay (which was afterwards baked either by sun or fire), many of them four thousand years ago. No correction or erasure can have been made in them since that date. A translation of one of these tablets as given at p. 75 in the *Guide to the Nimroud Central Saloon*, is here given as an example of the style of many others.

"No. 3. Tablet and outer case inscribed with a deed of partnership or brotherhood between Ṣini-Innanna and Iriba^{m}-Sin.

"Tablet. Ṣini-Innanna and Iriba^{m}-Sin made brotherhood; they took a judge for the ratification, and went down to the temple of the sun-god, and he answered the people thus in the temple of the sun-god: 'They must give Arda-luštâmar-Šamaš and Antu-lišlimam, the property of Iraba^{m}-šin, and Ârdu-ibšînan and Antu-am-anna-lamazi, the property of Ṣini-Innanna.' He proclaimed [also] in the temple of the sun-god and the moon-god: 'Brother shall be kind to brother; brother shall not be evil towards, shall not injure, brother; and brother shall not harbour any angry thought as to anything about which a brother has disputed.'

"They have invoked the name of Innannaki, Utu, Marduk,

But, further, there are astrological works copied for the library of Assurbanipal from ancient Babylonian originals. The compilation of many of these originals is placed by scholars in the reign of Sargon of Accad,[1] at the remote date of 3,800 B.C.

Lugal-ki-ušuna, and the name of Ḫammurabi [Kîmta-rapaštu] the king."

Here follow the names of eight witnesses. The translation of the inscription on the outer case is much to the same purpose, and need not here be quoted; the names of nine witnesses are appended to it. The *Guide* continues, after some other explanations, as follows:

"The whole of the first paragraph (except a few ideographs) is in Semitic Babylonian. The invocation is in Akkadian. The list of 'witnesses,' again, is in Semitic Babylonian, *and the date in Akkadian*. . . . The tablet is dated in the same way as the other documents of this class: 'Month Adar of the year when Ḫammurabi the king made (images of) Innanna and Nanâ.'"

[1] Sargon I. of Accad was of Semitic race. He was established as ruler in the city of Accad, and there reigned over a great non-Semitic race, in ancient cuneiform inscriptions styled the *Accadai* (Accadians). This word, as scholars tell us, carried the meaning of "highlanders," or "mountaineers." From this fact it is inferred they were not indigenous to the low plain surrounding the city of Accad, to which they gave their name. Their language contains few words for the productions of the almost tropical climate of Babylonia, but it shows familiarity with those of higher latitudes. At the time when Sargon, either by peaceful or warlike arts, was established as ruler over the Accadians, they were already a very highly civilized people. They possessed a literature of their own, which embraced a wide variety of subjects. The learning of the Accadians was highly esteemed,

In these ancient astrological works, the same calendar referred to in the trade documents, and in the late Babylonian almanacs, appears to obtain. We find in them the same year of twelve lunar months, reinforced at intervals by a thirteenth intercalated month, and, which is very important, the order of the months is always the same. Nisan (Accadian Barzig-gar), everywhere appears as "the first month," and is distinctly stated to be "the beginning of the year."[1]

As early as the year 1874, Professor Sayce pointed out that there was good reason for supposing that the twelve Babylonian months corresponded to the twelve divisions of the Zodiac. At page 161 of his Paper, *The Astronomy and*

and translations into the Semitic language were made of important religious and scientific Accadian works. These works, down to the latest days of Babylonian power, were preserved and venerated, and many copies of them were made and preserved in public libraries in Babylonia and Assyria.

The Accadian after Sargon's date gradually dropped out of general use, and became a "learned" language, holding amongst Babylonians and Assyrians much the same position as Latin and Greek amongst Europeans.

[1] See *Transactions of the Society of Biblical Archæology*, 1874. Paper entitled, *The Astronomy and Astrology of the Babylonians*, Prof. Sayce, p. 258, W.A.I. iii. 60.

Astrology of the Babylonians, we read: "Now a slight inspection of the calendar will show that the Accadian months derived their names from the signs of the Zodiac."

He then proceeds to discuss and compare the meanings of the Accadian and Semitic month names, and to point out those in which a reference to the Zodiac might most clearly be traced.

That the constellations of the Zodiac were from a remote age recognized by the dwellers in Mesopotamia is scarcely to be doubted. We find on the boundary stones in the British Museum *representations* of several of their figures. The Bull, the Tortoise (in lieu of the Crab), a female figure with wings, the Scorpion, the Archer, and the Goat-fish, are all portrayed, not only on boundary stones, but also on cylinder seals and gems.

Again, in the old astrological works, we find *mention* of the Scorpion "Gir-tab," and of the Goat-fish "Muna-xa," and as planets are said to "approach to," and "linger in," the stars of Gir-tab and of Muna-xa, it may well be supposed that they were the Zodiacal constellations still represented under the forms of Scorpion and Goat-fish.

Out of the many star-groups mentioned in the old tablets, only a few have as yet been certainly identified with their modern equivalents. As to the identity of others, we may guess. For instance, when it is said "Mercury[1] lingered in the constellation Gula," we may guess that Gula represents Aquarius, which sign in the Epping and Strassmaier tablets figures as "Gu."

From all these sources of information, we gather that the twelve divisions of the ecliptic had been mapped out at the time the astrological works were drawn up, and that some (at least) of these divisions corresponded exactly to those now represented on celestial globes.

The suggestion, therefore, put forward by Professor Sayce and other scholars, that the twelve Accadian months corresponded to the twelve constellations of the Zodiac, and that we may trace a resemblance in some instances between the name of the month in the old Accadian language and the constellation into which the sun at that time of the year entered, is not in itself improbable.

[1] *Infra*, p. 47, note.

The following months are those in which this resemblance is very striking:

1st month, Bar zig-gar ("the sacrifice of righteousness"), Aries.

2nd month, Khar-sidi ("the propitious bull"), Taurus.

3rd month (sometimes called) Kas ("the Twins"), Gemini.

6th month, Ki Gingir-na ("the errand of Istar"), Virgo.

We know from the Epping and Strassmaier tablets as a matter of fact, that the months and the constellations of the Zodiac *did* in the second century, B.C., correspond with each other in order and sequence as above suggested, and if further research should establish the fact that they so corresponded in Sargon's time, then as we find Nisan (Bar zig-gar) throughout all these ages holding the place of "first month," and marking "the beginning of the year," it will necessarily follow that the Accadian, Babylonian, and Assyrian calendars dealt with a *sidereal* and not a *tropical* year.

Ours is a *tropical* year, that is to say, according

to the Julian calendar (afterwards amended by Pope Gregory) it is bound to the *seasons*, and its months maintain a constant relation to the four great divisions of the ecliptic, *i.e.* the solstices and the equinoxes. The winter solstice always falls about the 22nd of December, the spring equinox about the 21st of March, the summer solstice about the 21st of June, and the autumnal equinox about the 23rd of September.

But (as has been suggested) the Accadian year was a *sidereal* year, and its months maintained a constant relation to the twelve *star-marked* divisions of the ecliptic, or, as they are called, the constellations of the Zodiac. Nisan always corresponded (as closely as a lunar month might) to the time during which the sun traversed the constellation Aries; Airu to the time during which it traversed the constellation Taurus; and so on through the twelve months of the year.

The equinoctial points are, however, always, though slowly, changing their position amongst the twelve constellations of the ecliptic. The months, therefore, which in 3,800 B.C., and still in the second century B.C., corresponded to the same star-groups, as above noted, must have held in different ages very different positions in regard to the four great divisions or *seasons* of the year.

We find in the tablets translated by Epping and Strassmaier the year "*beginning with Nisan, hence in the spring*," and this seems a more or less natural season from which to count the year; but when, taking the precession of the equinoxes into account, we find that the year in Ḫammurabi's time (2,200 B.C.) must have commenced one month, and in Sargon's time (3,800 B.C.) two months before the spring equinox, we feel surprised and perplexed to find that the year must then have begun without any reference to the seasons—the four great and most easily observed divisions of the ecliptic.

It is difficult to imagine that the astronomers who so skilfully divided the ecliptic into its twelve parts, and who originated the wonderful Accadian calendar—a calendar so well thought out that, as we have seen reason to believe, it resisted all the shocks of time for nearly four thousand years—it is difficult to imagine that such astronomers should have taken no note of the four prominent divi-

PLATE I.

FIG. 1.

FIG. 2.

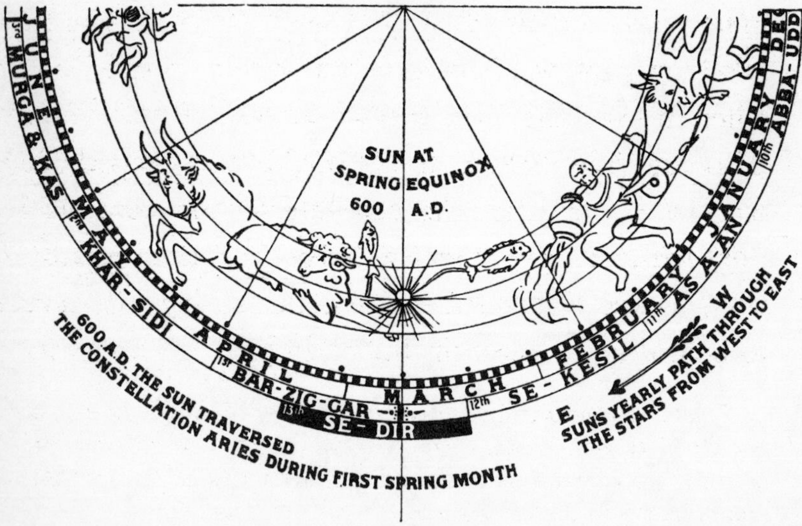

The first and last months of the Accadian, sidereal, year, compared with the months of the Gregorian, tropical, year: at 6,000 B.C. and at 600 A.D.

[*To face p.* 13.

sions of the year and of the ecliptic, *i.e.* the solstices and the equinoxes.

There is, however, a way to account for this anomaly, or, rather, there is a supposition which, if adopted, will allow these astronomers of old to have taken note, not only of the *months*, but also of the *seasons* of the year, when first they drew up their mighty scheme.

Let us suppose that the calendar which, as we may learn from the astrological tablets, was already in Sargon's time a well known and venerated institution, had been originally drawn up at a date much earlier than Sargon's, when the first month (Bar zig-gar), was not the first *spring* month, but when it was the first *winter* month of the year. This date (see Plate I., fig. 1) would have been about 6,000 B.C.; for then the sun entered the constellation Aries at the *winter solstice*—a season equally well, if not better suited than the spring equinox to hold the first place in the calendar.[1] Under this

[1] After this paper had appeared in the *Proceedings of the Society of Biblical Archæology*, a corroboration of this opinion occurred to the writer's mind, suggested by a further study of the month names in the Accadian calendar. It is as follows:—

The twelfth month is named "sowing of seed." Seed may be

supposition, it would no longer be difficult to imagine why the ancient Accadian astronomers should have chosen Aries as the first constellation of the Zodiac, and Nisan (Bar zig-gar) as the first month, and the "beginning of the year."

Nor need we throw discredit on the early

and is, sown in many latitudes in *spring*, and also in *winter* time. "Sowing of seed" might therefore describe a month at the ending of an equinoctial or of a solstitial year: but the thirteenth (*i.e.* the occasionally intercalated) month is named that of "dark sowing." This epithet *dark*, added to the "sowing" of the twelfth month, very plainly points to a solstitial or midwinter ending of the year.

The thirteenth month in a luni-solar year, whose beginning should be bound to the vernal equinox, must always cover some of the concluding days of March and some of the first days of April; and those days are certainly much *lighter*, *not darker* than those of the preceding month, covering parts of February and March, whereas, the thirteenth intercalary month in a luni-solar year, whose beginning should be bound to the winter solstice, must always cover the concluding days of December and those at the beginning of January; and might well be distinguished by the epithet *dark*, not only from the days of the preceding month, but indeed from those of any other month of the year (see Plate I., figs. 1, 2.)

It is of interest here to note that this insistence in Accadian month nomenclature on the darkness of the thirteenth month, tends to confirm the already formed opinion of scholars, that the Accadians were not indigenous to Babylonia, but had descended into it from more northern latitudes, where darkness is a more marked concomitant of winter than in the nearly tropical latitude of Babylonia.

calendar makers 6,000 B.C., if we take for granted that they were not acquainted with the fact that slowly but inevitably the seasons must change their position amongst the stars, and that, not knowing this, they believed that in making the *beginning of the year* dependent on the sun's entry into the *constellation Aries*, they were also binding it to the *season of the winter solstice.*

As centuries rolled by, however, and slowly the stars of Aries receded from the winter solstice, Bar zig-gar was no longer the first month in the sense of being the first winter month. Still, the authority of the originators of the calendar held sway; provision had been only made for counting the year as a sidereal year; and Bar zig-gar, or the month in which the sun entered Aries, was still called the first month, and looked on as the beginning of the year.

To carry out the reformation of any long established calendar is, we know, not a trifling undertaking. Even on secular grounds, any proposed reform encounters strong opposition. But the calendar in Babylonia was not only a civil, it was also a religious, institution. Its origin was attributed to the Creator, and as the work of the Creator, it is described in one of the old Babylonian tablets.[1]

"For each of the twelve months HE fixed three stars" (or groups of stars). "From the day when the year issues forth to the close."[2]

The astronomical and astrological texts drawn up for Sargon of Accad are entitled "The Illumination of Bel,"[3] and still as late as the second century B.C., all Babylonian almanacs bore the heading: "At the command of my Lord Bel and my Lady Beltis, a decree."[4] Thus it was, we may suppose, that under the protection of the gods the Accadian calendar continued unchanged throughout all the changing ages.

[1] *Records of the Past.* New series. Vol. i. p. 145.

[2] In modern works we find the terms "useless," "fanciful," and "inconvenient," applied to the Zodiac and its constellations; and for regulating a tropical year the constellations *are* "useless" and "inconvenient," but the theory that the reckoning of the year and all its religious festivals depended on the observance of the Zodiacal star-groups, would help to account for the widely spread veneration in which they were held throughout so many ages and by so many nations.

[3] *Transactions of the Society of Biblical Archæology*, 1874, pp. 150, 151.

[4] Epping and Strassmaier, *Astronomisches aus Babylon*, p. 161. (*Auf Geheiss von Bel und Beltis meiner Herrin, eine Entscheidung.*)

But during all the ages the winter solstice moved on steadily through almost a quarter of the great circle of the ecliptic,[1] and in the second century B.C., the *spring equinox* was not far from the same point of the star-marked ecliptic where

[1] This moving of the equinoctial point through a *quarter* of the great circle may perhaps explain the tradition to which Syncellus twice alludes, once when he states that Eusebius was aware of the Greek opinion that many ages, or rather myriads of years had passed since the creation of the world, *during the mythical retrograde movement of the Zodiac, from the beginning of Aries, and its return again to the same point* (*Chronographia*, p. 17.)

And again at p. 52, he refers to "the return of the Zodiac to its original position, according to the stories of the Greeks and Egyptians, that is to say, the revolution from one point back again to the same point, which is the first minute of the first division of the equinoctial sign of the Zodiac, which is called κριὸς (Aries) by them, as has been stated in the *Genica* of Hermes and in the Cyrannid books."

He goes on to say that this is the ground of the chronological division of Claudius Ptolemy.

Jean Silvain Bailly, speaking of the Indian Zodiac, the beginning of which is placed by the Brahmins at the first point of Aries, suggests that a similar tradition may have prevailed amongst the Indians and other ancient nations to account for the pre-eminence so generally accorded to Aries. He says:

"Mais pourquoi ont-ils choisi cette constellation pour la première? Il est évident que c'est une affaire de préjugé et de superstition ; le choix du premier point dans un cercle est arbitraire. Ils auront été décidés par quelque ancienne tradition, telle par example que celle que Muradi rapporte d'après Albumassar et deux anciens livres égyptiens, où on lisoit que le monde avoit été

the *winter solstice* had been when first the calendar-makers had "fixed" the constellations "for the twelve months from the day when the year issues forth to the close," and we who now read the almanacs drawn up at that late period of Babylonian history are not (as has been said above) surprised to find the year "*beginning with Nisan, hence in the spring.*" (See Plate I., fig. 2.)

The propositions contained in this Paper are these :—

I. The Accadian year was counted as a sidereal year.

II. The Accadian calendar was first thought out and originated at a date not later than 6,000 B.C.

The first proposition is founded on the opinion,

renouvellé après le déluge lorsque le soleil étoit au 1° du bélier, régulus étant dans le colure des solstices. D'Herbelot ne parle point de régulus; mais il dit que selon Albumassar les sept planetes étoient en conjonction au premier point du bélier lors de la création du monde. Cette tradition, sans doute fabuleuse, qui venoit des mêmes préjugés que celle de Bérose, étoit asiatique. Elle a pu suffire, ou telle autre du même genre, pour fonder la préférence que les brames, ou les anciens en général, ont donnée à la constellation du bélier, en l'établissant la première de leur zodiaque. Ils ont cru que ce point du zodiaque étoit une source de renouvellement, et ils ont dit que le zodiaque et l'année se renouvelloient au même point où le monde s'étoit régénéré." (Bailly, *Histoire de l'Astronomie Ancienne*, pp. 482, 483.)

long ago expressed by many Oriental scholars, that the Accadian months corresponded in very early ages with the constellations of the Zodiac, Nisan —the month during which the sun was in conjunction with the constellation Aries—holding the first place then, as also in the latest times of Babylonian history, and, presumably, through the intervening period.

But even if the first proposition is granted, the second, it must be confessed, is only an opinion based on the unlikelihood that the old Accadian and sidereal year, otherwise so skilfully dealt with in the calendar, should have begun, in what would appear to be a haphazard manner, at no definite season of the year.

It may seem that too much weight has been attached in this Paper to what can only be called a guess; but where there is so much that we desire to know, and so little as yet absolutely known of the early history of astronomy, the temptation to make such guesses is great.

It is to their earliest heroes and to their gods that the ancient heathen nations attributed the invention of astronomy, and amongst the Jews also, according to Josephus, the children of Seth were looked upon as being the first teachers of the science.[1]

Modern astronomers often speak in general terms of their science as having existed in a "hoar antiquity," and in "prehistoric times." But questions as to when, and where it took its rise, are still unanswered. During the last hundred years these questions have been keenly discussed. Babylon, Egypt, Greece, India, and China, have each been claimed as "the cradle" of the science. Some few writers (and prominent amongst them Jean Silvain Bailly, a brilliant scholar and an eminent astronomer) have contended for the view that not by any one nation were the chief advances in astronomy made, but that before the great races of mankind separated from the parent stock, and spread themselves over the globe, the phenomena of astronomy had been closely observed, and scientific methods for measuring time had been adopted. Bailly speaks of "une astronomie perfectionnée," of which only "les débris" are to be met with in possession of the civilized races of

[1] *Antiquitates Judaicæ*, I. 2, § 3.

antiquity. He claims an antediluvian race as the originators of astronomic science.

It may seem a bold suggestion to place the formation of the calendar at a date so high as 6,000 B.C., a date exceeding as it does by 2,000 years that given to us in the margin of our Bibles for the story of the fall of man and his expulsion from Eden. It was in following Archbishop Usher's calculations that the date of 4,004 was adopted and placed, where it still remains, in our English Bibles. But the difficulty of determining the early dates of Bible history has always been felt to be very great, and "it is quite possible to believe that Genesis gives us no certain data for pronouncing on the time of man's existence on the earth."[1] Scholars, in basing their calculations on the authority of Scripture, have arrived at very different conclusions. Some only demand 3,616, others 6,984 years, as required from Scriptural sources for "the years of the world to the birth of Christ."[2]

[1] Introduction to the Pentateuch, by E. Harold Browne, D.D., Bishop of Ely. Holy Bible, with Commentary, edited by F. C. Cook, M.A., Canon of Exeter.

[2] The following extracts are taken from the Preface to *An Universal History from the Earliest Account of Time to the Present:*

It will be seen that the earlier of these dates leads us back to an even more remote age than that in which, if the theory here proposed is a true one, the marvellous achievement of the formation of a scientific sidereal calendar was accomplished.

To attribute to the dwellers in Eden or to their immediate descendants intellectual gifts that should enable them to perfect so grand a scheme, does certainly not contradict the story of the fall, but

Compiled from Original Authors [*Etc.*]. *Dublin: Printed by Edward Bate for the Editors: M,DCC,XLIV.*

They are interesting as showing that even before archæological research had extended the limits of ancient history, as it has done during the last fifty years, many biblical scholars assigned a far higher date than Archbishop Usher's 4,004 years for the history of Adam's race on earth.

P. lxv. *et seq.*: "So that on a strict view and due examination of the antiquities of nations, and the records that have been left us, those of the Jews, exclusive of their divine authority, will evidently appear to be the most certain and authentick. . . . However it must be confessed that there is no certain uniformity in the Jewish computation, and that the several copies of their records, *viz.*, the Hebrew, Samaritan Pentateuch, and Septuagint differ very much from one another. . . . This variety of computations hath left room for Chronologers to enlarge or contract the space of time betwixt the flood and the birth of Christ, by adhering to one copy rather than another; or by rejecting or retaining the whole numbers, or the particulars, just as it suited their humour of making the Sacred History agree with the Prophane; or otherwise of reducing the Prophane to the Sacred, and as the disagreement among the heathen writers is great also, and every author hath followed the historian he liked best, hence a wide difference rather may open up for us fresh lines of thought, when we read of that transgression in which the pride of intellect played so important a part.

hath arisen amongst modern Chronologers as appears by the various computations . . . which we here give as collected by Strauchius, Chevreau, and others. It would be endless as well as unnecessary here to examine into the particular causes of this great difference amongst authors, every one still pretending to ground his system on the authority of the Scripture.

A Table of the years of the world to the birth of Christ, according to the computations of several chronologers.

Alphonsus, King of Castile, in Muller's Tables .	6,984	
The same, in Strauchius	6,484	9 months
Onuphrius Panvinius	6,310	
Suidas	6,000	
Lactantius, Philastrius	5,801	
Nicephorus	5,700	
Clemens Alexandrinus	5,624	
The author of the Fasti Siculi	5,608	9 months
Isaac Vossius, and the Greeks	5,598	
Etc. etc."	"	

II

THE CONSTELLATION ARIES

[Reprinted from the *Proceedings of the Society of Biblical Archæology, March* 1893]

In the January number of the *Proceedings of the Society of Biblical Archæology* for last year, under the title *The Accadian Calendar*, two propositions were advanced :—

I. The Accadian year was counted as a sidereal year.

II. The Accadian calendar was first thought out and originated at a date not later than 6,000 B.C.

The fact that the sun's entry into the constellation Aries appears to have marked through many millenniums the beginning of the Accadian year, was cited in support of the first proposition, and the fact that the sun's entry into Aries coincided about 6,000 B.C. with the winter solstice, was relied on to support the probability of the second proposition, namely, that at the above date the calendar, which so honoured the inconspicuous constellation Aries, was first drawn up.

If we now find this inconspicuous part of the heavens equally honoured by several nations in very ancient times, we shall be led to think either that these nations, independently of each other, happened to observe and mark out the sun's annual course through the heavens at exactly the same date, and therefore chose the same point as marking the winter solstice; or we must suppose that they derived their calendar and knowledge of the Zodiac from observations originally made by some *one* civilized race.

The Brahmins of India claim a high antiquity for the science of astronomy in their country, and their observations and calculations profess to date back to the fourth millennium B.C. The names of the Indian constellations are preserved to us in the Sanscrit language, and these names are, so to speak, identical with those that we use at the present day when we speak of the figures of the Zodiac. Many scholars of to-day believe that only after Alexander's conquests in India did the knowledge of the twelve-fold division of the Zodiac penetrate into that country. Some, on the other hand, maintain the opposite opinion, namely, "that the names of the signs can be proved to have existed in India at as early a period as in any other country."[1]

Jean Silvain Bailly, whose opinions as to the antiquity of the science of astronomy have been already quoted in the foregoing Paper, in his work on the history of ancient astronomy, speaking of the Brahmins of India, the initial point of whose Zodiac is at the first star in the constellation Aries, writes as follows :[2]—

[1] V. p. 90.

[2] The initial point of the Hindu Zodiac (see Plate III.) is about 9½ degrees to the west of the boundary line of the constellation Aries, as it is drawn on our celestial globes. One foot of Aries, however, extends beyond the boundary line, and touches a line drawn through the initial point of the Hindu Zodiac and the poles of the ecliptic. At page 132, the question of the date of the fixation of this initial point is discussed, and a high antiquity for it is claimed. There are many considerations which may lead us to the opinion that not only in India, but amongst the ancients generally, the first degree of the constellation coincided with the Hindu initial point, and not with the boundary line of the constellation, as it is now drawn. Greek and Latin authors, writing in the first century B.C., speak of the solstitial and equinoctial colures, as being "at the eighth degree of the Zodiac," and these

"Mais pourquoi ont-ils choisi cette constellation pour la première? Il est évident que c'est une affaire de préjugé et de superstition; le choix du premier point dans un cercle est arbitraire. Ils auront été décidés par quelque ancienne tradition."

Dupuis, writing at nearly the same date as Bailly, about a hundred years ago, and in conflict with him on many points relating to the Zodiac, was also struck by the choice of this same inconspicuous point in the great circle of the ecliptic, not only by the Brahmins of India, but also by other ancient nations. He further explains that the difference in the choice of initial point by the Chinese, and by the other nations, is only an apparent, and not a real difference. On the wonderful agreement shown by so many nations, in their choice of the stars by which they marked the beginning of their Zodiacs, Dupuis relied to

statements, which have caused modern commentators much perplexity (see *Handbuch der Klassischen Alterthumswissenschaft; Zeitrechnung der Griechen und Römer*, Unger), may be easily explained, if we realize that they, in all likelihood, counted the degrees of the Zodiac from the same initial point as that in use amongst Hindu astronomers, which in the first century B.C. was eight degrees to the west of the equinoctial point.

support his views concerning the unity of the astronomical and religious myths of all nations.

At the end of his work, *Mémoire Explicatif du Zodiaque*, Dupuis gives in a diagram several Zodiacs in concentric circles; some divided into twelve, some into twenty-seven or twenty-eight parts. He represents the colures by a cross which quarters these concentric Zodiacs, and speaking of the twenty-seven- and twenty-eight-fold divisions, he observes as follows:

"On remarque d'abord, que ces divers systèmes lunaires, tirés de l'Astronomie de différens peuples, s'accordent tous à placer dans les cases correspondantes à-peu-près les mêmes étoiles. Il suffit, pour s'en assurer, de comparer les étoiles designées dans la même case de la division de chaque peuple. On remarque aussi qu'ils ont pris tous, excepté les Chinois, les mêmes étoiles, pour point initial de la division, savoir, celles de la tête du Bélier. Les Chinois, au contraire, ont fixé le point initial dans la partie du ciel diamétralement opposée, vers les pieds de la Vierge et pres l'Epi" (p. 4).

Dupuis' arguments, drawn from the choice by several nations of the first division of Aries as the initial point of the Zodiac and year, are of equal cogency in support of a calendar such as he suggests, drawn up more than 12,000 B.C., for a year beginning at the *autumn equinox;* or for a calendar, as suggested in this Paper, drawn up about 6,000 B.C., and dealing with a year beginning at the *winter solstice;* and it may be claimed that the facts brought to light by the study of the ancient Accadian calendar, while greatly strengthening the ground for Dupuis' opinion concerning the early acceptance by many nations of the stars of Aries as a mark for the beginning of the year in prehistoric times, seem more in favour of the first month of that year having been counted from the *winter solstice* than from the *autumn equinox.*

Quotations from authors like Bailly and Dupuis may seem nowadays somewhat out of date; for though they were amongst the foremost scholars of their time, they were necessarily ignorant of all the archæological discoveries that have succeeded each other with such rapidity during the last century. Unless, therefore, the brilliant guesses and astronomical speculations of these writers can find confirmation in the results of modern researches, their theories may well be disregarded.

But it seems to me that many of their theories are meeting with such confirmation.

Turning first to some of the facts which archæology has taught us regarding the ancient Egyptians, it will be interesting to see if there are any indications in their astronomy or mythology of honour paid to the constellation Aries in connexion with the progress of the sun and moon through the figures of the Zodiac.

It is true that the acquaintance of the ancient Egyptians with these figures is a matter still in dispute, and the various methods of counting the year followed by them also present great difficulties to scholars. It is, however, admitted that they were a people much given to the observation and worship of the heavenly bodies, and that their astronomy and mythology were very closely interwoven with each other.

In the time of the Middle Empire, it seems, the months in the civil year were not counted as lunar months, but as months of thirty days each. The year was not counted as a sidereal year, but as one of three hundred and sixty days —twelve months of thirty days—with five days added at the end of each year to bring up the number to three hundred and sixty-five days. No attention was paid to the odd hours and minutes over and above the three hundred and sixty-five days, which are occupied by the sun in completing his annual course.

Mr Griffiths has remarked in the number of the *Proceedings of the Society of Biblical Archæology* for March 1892, that the hieroglyph for month points to an *originally* lunar month, and I would suggest that the star under the first crescent seems to point also to a month originally counted sidereally, *i.e.*, dependent upon the conjunction of the sun and moon in some particular star-group of the ecliptic. As a matter of fact, the Egyptians made use not only of a civil year such as has been above described, but also of a sidereal year, counted from the heliacal rising of Sirius, and it is perhaps possible that the months in this sidereal year were counted as lunar months, and the year treated as soli-lunar and sidereal.

In these two Egyptian *calendars*—so far as they are at present understood—no reference to the constellation Aries seems to be discernible.

The agricultural importance of the season of the summer solstice in Egypt, coinciding as it does with the rising of the Nile, may have induced calendar-makers at some very early date to re-arrange the order of the year, so as to make it begin at the *summer* rather than the *winter* solstice—the season, as it is contended in these Papers, originally chosen 6,000 B.C. by astronomers in a more northern latitude than that of Egypt as the starting-point of a year sidereally marked by the conjunction of the sun with the constellation Aries.

But if we turn to the Egyptian *mythology*, the importance of the Ram, or rather of the head of the Ram, as it is revealed in the monuments, and in the pictorial art of the ancient Egyptians, must continually strike the student of Egyptian symbolism.

Amen, the great god of the Theban triad (Amen, Maut, and Chons), is sometimes represented as ram-headed—his boat and his sceptre are always adorned with a ram's head, and the great temple to him, in conjunction with the sun, *i.e.* to Amen-Ra, is approached through an avenue of gigantic ram-headed sphinxes, and this is also the case as regards the temple of Chons—the

moon-god—at right angles, and in close proximity, to the great temple of Amen-Ra.

Scholars tell us that Horus, Isis, and Osiris, —the Memphian triad—symbolized the *diurnal* motion of the sun and other heavenly bodies, and it need not appear improbable that the great Theban triad, Amen, Maut, and Chons, should have originally symbolized the *annual* course of those same bodies through the constellations of the Zodiac. This would account for the prominence of the Ram in connexion with the worship of this triad—the Ram, which, as I have argued, in many countries, and possibly in Egypt also, marked the first division of the Zodiac and year.

A prayer to Amen is translated by G. Maspero in the April number for 1891 of the *Proceedings of the Society of Biblical Archæology*;[1] from this translation it would appear that Amen is implored to bring the calendar into touch with the real seasons of the year. If Amen represented a

[1] "Il ne me reste plus qu'à donner la traduction suivie du texte (Papyrus Anastasi, iv., p. 10. L 1-5), dont je viens d'expliquer le sens et le développement littéraire.

"Viens à moi, Amon, me délivrer de l'année fâcheuse, où le dieu Shou (Shou était, à l'époque des Ramessides et plus tard, le dieu du soleil solstitial, du soleil d'été, comme Brugsch l'a

sidereally marked point in the yearly course of the sun, such a prayer might suitably have been addressed to him by the Egyptians.

The great temple to Amen-Ra at Thebes, approached, as has been stated above, through an avenue of ram-headed sphinxes, is oriented to the setting sun of the season so important to Egyptians, that of the summer solstice, and this fact strengthens the opinion that Amen was considered to be a god in some way presiding over the course of the year and its right measurement. It is true that this orientation of his temple precluded the possibility of the light from any star of the constellation Aries ever shining into the shrine of the god; but it is perhaps possible that the ceremony of "the great

montré fort ingénieusement) ne se lève plus, où vient l'hiver où était l'été, où les mois s'en vont hors leur place, où les heures se brouillent, où les grands t'appellent, ô Amon, où les petits te cherchent, où ceux même qui sont encore dans les bras de leur nourrice, ceux-là (crient): 'Donne les souffles!'—Amon trouve Amon écoute, Amon est le sain devant qui marchent les souffles agréables; il me donne d'être comme l'aile du vautour, comme la palette chargée des discours des Esprits pour les bergers dans les champs, pour les laveurs sur la berge, pour les garde-chasse qui sortent au territoire des gazelles afin de lacer (le gibier)."

M. Maspero states that the latter lines of the text are injured and difficult to decipher or to understand.

feast-day of Amon Father," described by Ebers, may have been devised by the votaries of Amen as a means whereby they could honour the god, as one presiding over the most propitious season of the year, and also recall the sidereal connexion of the god of the year with the, from times immemorial highly reverenced, constellation Aries.

At pp. 277 and 278 of *Egypt, Descriptive, Historical, and Picturesque*, vol. ii., Ebers, having referred to some figures represented on the walls of a Memnonium in the Nekropolis erected by Rameses II., exactly opposite to the Great Temple of Karnak, observes :—

"Of these figures the inscription says :—'As they approach the king their arms are filled with choice produce and stores, and all the good things that the earth brings forth are gathered by them to add to the joy on the great feast-day of Amon, the father.'"

"These words refer to the great 'feast of the Valley' (*heb en-ant*), when, on the 29th day of the second month of the inundation, the statue of Amon was brought forth from the sanctuary with much magnificence and solemnity, and conveyed across the Nile to the Nekropolis, that the god might there offer sacrifices to his ancestors in the other world. The priests of the house of Seti received the procession with the splendid bark Sam, the most sacred of all the vessels that were preserved in the temple of Karnak: in this the statue of the god was placed, and borne first to the Memnonium of Seti, and then round about the Nekropolis, preceded by a crowd of temple servants, who strewed the way with sand. The solemnities ended with a grand nocturnal spectacle, on the great sacred lake of which traces may still be seen to the extreme south of the Nekropolis.

"The Egyptian religion prescribed to all its followers that they should visit the tombs of their dead and bring offerings, in grateful remembrance of their parents and forefathers; and as, day after day, millions of suns had gone to rest—as men do—behind the realm of tombs in the Libyan hills, the god himself was brought to do honour to his departed ancestry, and to sacrifice to them."

The rising of the Nile in Egypt coincides very closely with the season of the *summer solstice*. At the date of Rameses II.—a date not yet unanimously agreed on by scholars, but which may be safely placed between 1,400 and 1,100 B.C.—the sun at the season of the *summer solstice* was in the constellation Cancer (see Plate II.), and

PLATE II.

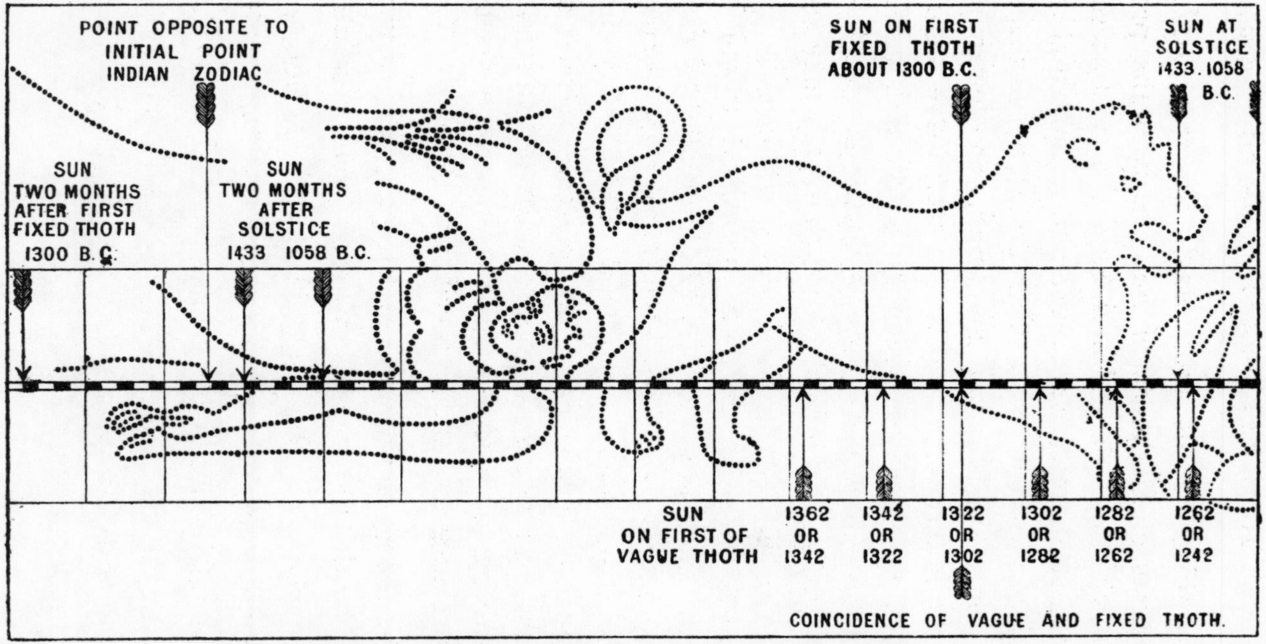

Relating to "the Feast-day of Amon, the Father."

Position of sun on first of fixed Thoth varied by about one degree in two hundred years.

[*To face p.* 36.

two months later its place in the ecliptic was a few degrees to the west of a point exactly opposed to the first stars of Aries and to the initial point of the Indian Zodiac. On the evening, therefore, of the 29th day of the second month of the inundation, when the sun had now sunk behind the Libyan hills, and daylight had faded sufficiently to allow them to show their light,[1] the first stars of Aries rose above the eastern horizon, and at midnight attained to the southern meridian.

Thus at the season of all the year, when Aries specially dominated the ecliptic, the statue of the god Amen was, as we learn, brought out of his dark temple shrine and carried in procession to the Nekropolis, from whence the constellation Aries — not hidden by obstructing walls and columns—was fully visible; and there honour was done and sacrifice offered to "Amon Father."

But it may be said that we should understand "the second month of the inundation"

[1] When the sun is about 7° below the western horizon, stars in the opposite quarter of the heavens begin to be visible.

to refer to the second month of the Egyptian sidereal year counted from the 1st Thoth (fixed) and marked by the heliacal rising of Sirius. At the date of Rameses the beginning of this sidereal year fell, as may be proved, a fortnight after the *summer solstice* (see Plate II.), and still on the 29th of the second month of this sidereal year the stars of Aries might be seen rising in the east—no longer only its first stars, but nearly the whole constellation then becoming visible — and at about midnight its brightest stars, α and β Arietis, culminated on the meridian. Whether, therefore, the "Feast of the Valley" was held at the end of the second month of the actual inundation, or of the second month of the sidereal year, the stars of Aries presided over its "nocturnal" solemnities.

Some scholars claim, however, that all Egyptian festivals were swept round through the seasons, and the stars that marked those seasons, in the course of fourteen or fifteen hundred years, inasmuch as they were firmly bound to the *vague* calendrical year of 365 days. If this was indeed so, it would be difficult to imagine that Seti I. or Rameses II. could have established the festival in question as in any way connected with honour to be paid to the constellation Aries; for though during the reign of Seti, and perhaps during the early part of that of Rameses, the vague and fixed years coincided more or less closely (see Plate II.), yet before the death of Rameses they were already so far apart that the 1st Thoth (vague) fell, not a fortnight later than the summer solstice, but about a fortnight earlier; and therefore on the 29th day of the second month of the vague year the stars of Aries would not have risen until long after sunset, nor would any one of them have culminated on the meridian at midnight.

If now we turn our attention to the temple to Amen-Ra at Aboo Simbel, we may observe that, unlike that to the same god at Karnak, it is not oriented to any definite *season* of the year. The rising sun shines into it now, and must always have shone into the Holy of Holies of that rock-hewn temple on the morning of a day somewhat more than two months distant from the winter solstice, and somewhat less than a month before the season of the spring equinox, namely, on the morning of the 26th February (Gregorian).[1]

The sun now (1893 A.D.) is, at the season named, in the constellation Aquarius; but if we calculate back to a date anywhere between 1,400 and 1,100 B.C., we shall find (see Plate III.) that when Rameses II. dedicated this temple to

[1] "I was fortunate in seeing another wonderful thing during my visit to Aboo Simbel. The great temple is dedicated to Amen-Ra, the sun-god, and on two days in the year the sun is said to rise at such a point that it sends a beam of light through both halls till it falls on the shrine itself in the very Holy of Holies. Many theories are based on the orientation of the temples, and Captain Johnston wished to find on which day in the spring of the year the phenomenon took place; so he took his instruments, and we all went up to the temple before dawn. It was the 26th February. The great hall, with its eight Osiride pillars, was wrapped in semi-darkness. Still darker were the inner hall and shrine. Behind the altar sat the four gods, Amen, Horus, Ptah, and Rameses himself, now deified. All the East was a deep rosy flush; then that paled, and a hard white light filled the sky. Clearer and whiter it grew, till, with a sudden joyous rush, the sun swung up over the low ridge of hill, and in an instant, like an arrow from the bow of Phœbus Apollo, one level shaft of light pierced the great hall and fell in living glory straight upon the shrine itself."—A. F. [Extract from the *Pall Mall Gazette*, 20th April, 1892.]

PLATE III.

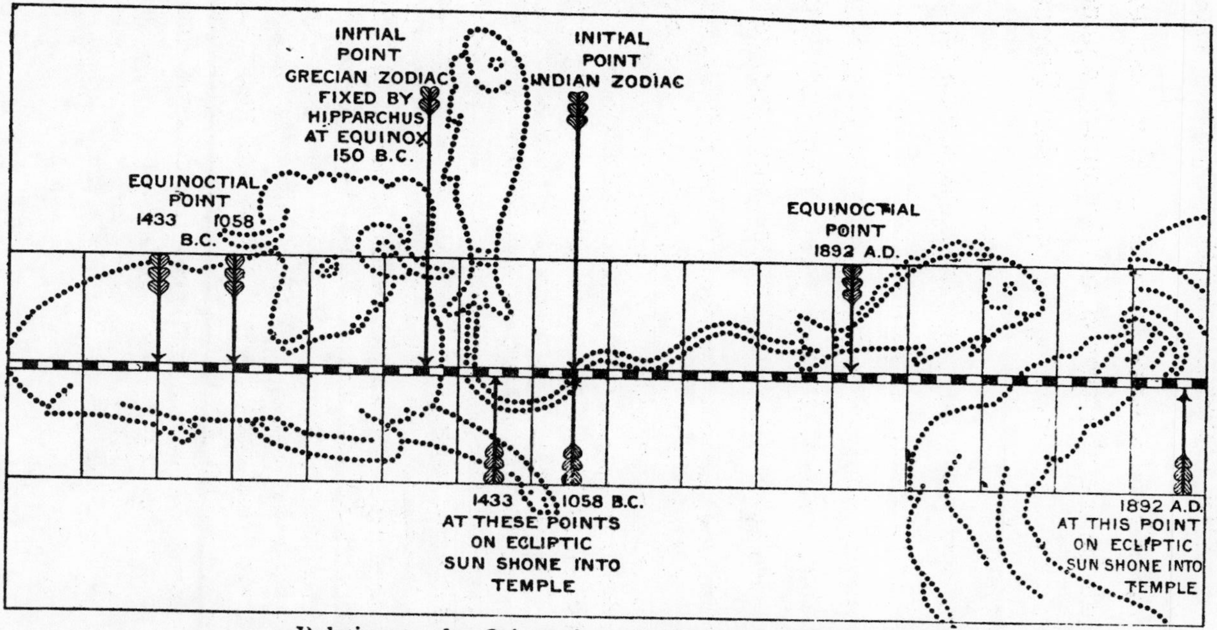

Relating to the Orientation of a Temple to Amon-Ra.

[*To face p.* 40.

Amen-Ra, the sun when it penetrated into the shrine of the temple at Aboo Simbel was in conjunction with the first stars of the constellation *Aries*, and this fact must, it would seem, encourage us to adopt the opinion put forward above concerning the desire of Rameses II. to honour that constellation in connexion with the god Amen.

It would seem then that there are indications in the mythology and in the history of the Egyptians, of honour paid to the constellation Aries, and as we further study the records of antiquity, now within our reach, it will, I believe, become evident that not only the Egyptians, but also all the great civilized nations of the East, had traditions of a year beginning when the sun and moon entered the constellation Aries—such a year as that in use amongst the Babylonians during their long existence as a nation, and such as that which is used by the Hindus in India to this present day.

If we allow weight to these considerations, it will be difficult to think that such a method of reckoning the year—involving, as it did, the recognition of the ecliptic star-groups under the fanciful figures of the Zodiac—should have been arrived at by each of these nations independently. Whether one nation borrowed these ideas from another, or whether some "earlier race of men" bequeathed this knowledge to their many descendants, is still an open question. Scholars have not unanimously awarded the palm of seniority in civilization to any one nation, and we are not at variance with proved facts, if we elect to adopt the theory of a common stock, from which the divergent races sprang. If, then, it should appear that these races possessed and incorporated into their mythologies a knowledge of the Zodiac, and of the first degree of Aries as its initial point, their separation from the parent stock must have been subsequent to the formation of the scheme that dealt with a calendar based on an observation of the colure of the winter solstice at that point, and under this supposition the date of 6,000 B.C. becomes a foothold for the chronology of ancient history. We should also be led to think of the common ancestors of the civilized races not as ignorant barbarians, but rather as men graced with high intellectual gifts—men whose teachings have been handed down through all the ages to this present day, and of whose imaginings the Zodiac remains as the most ancient monument of the work of intelligent man.

III

(*GU*), ELEVENTH CONSTELLATION OF THE ZODIAC

[Reprinted from the *Proceedings of the Society of Biblical Archæology, February* 1896]

IN the astronomical tablets (of the 1st and 2nd cent. B.C.) translated by Epping and Strassmaier, the twelve constellations of the Babylonian Zodiac are constantly referred to. Their names appear under very abbreviated forms in the tablets, and are as follows:[1]—

1. *(ku(sarikku))* = aries.
2. *(te(mennu))* = taurus.
3. *(mašu)* = gemini.
4. *(pulukku)* = cancer.
5. *(arū)* = leo.
6. *(serû)* = virgo.
7. *(zibanîtu)* = libra.
8. *(aqrabu)* = scorpio.
9. *(pa)* = arcitenens.
10. *(enzu)* = caper.
11. *(gu)* = amphora [aquarius].
12. *(zib)* = pisces.

[1] *Zeitschrift für Assyriologie,* v Band, 4 Heft, Oct. 1890, p. 351.

Also in Epping and Strassmaier's work, *Astronomisches aus Babylon*, under the heading *Die Zeichen des Thierkreises*, pp. 170, 171, and *Namen der Sterne*, pp. 174, 175, the twelve abbreviations met with in the tablets are discussed at some length.

From a study of the list here given and of the passages referred to, we learn that it has been found possible to suggest for some of the abbreviations suitable terminations, and in the completed words thus obtained, the familiar constellations of the Zodiac, as we know them, are easily to be recognized.

As regards other of the abbreviations, and amongst them that of  (Gu) for the eleventh sign (Amphora or Aquarius), no termination has been suggested; and of it Strassmaier thus writes:[1] p. 171:—"Gu ist sonst fast ausschliesslich nur als Silbenzeichen gu bekannt"; and Jensen, discussing Epping and Strassmaier's constellation list, writes thus of the abbreviation Gu for the eleventh constellation:[2] "Ob Gu einen 'Was-

[1] *Astronomisches aus Babylon.*

[2] *Kosmologie der Babylonier*, p. 314.

sereimer,' 'Schöpfeimer,' bezeichnen kann, weiss ich nicht. Die bisher veröffentlichten Texte geben keinen Aufschluss darüber."

As a probable completion for the abbreviation Gu, the following suggestion is here put forward :—

In the ancient astrological tablets translated by Professor Sayce in his Paper, *The Astronomy and Astrology of the Babylonians*,[1] pp. 189, 190, "the star of Gula" is mentioned. The first syllable of this word is composed of the same cuneiform group as that used in the abbreviation for the eleventh constellation of the Zodiac in the astronomical tablets of the first and second centuries B.C. above referred to. But this fact, if it stood alone, would not be enough to do more than point to a possible identification of Gu in the late tablets with Gula in the ancient astrological works. Amongst the many constellations in the heavens the name of more than one might have begun with the syllable Gu.

We find, however, at a later page (206) of Professor Sayce's Paper, this sentence translated from W.A.I., III. 57, 1 :—

[1] *Transactions*, *Biblical Archæology*, vol. iii., February 1874.

"Jupiter[1] in the star of Gula lingers." None of the five planets known to the Babylonians could ever with truth have been described as appearing or "lingering" in any part of the heavens outside the band of the Zodiac stars. "The star (or constellation) of Gula," we must therefore assume, was a Zodiacal star or constellation. This restriction of the position of the "star of Gula" renders it scarcely a rash conclusion to arrive at, that the *Zodiacal* Gu of the later tablets is an abbreviation for the *Zodiacal* Gula of the ancient astrological works.

As to a mythological reason for the choice of the goddess Gula to preside over the constellation known to us as Aquarius, we find it in the fact that Gula appears as another name for the goddess Bau[2] and Bau (or Bahu) was a personification of *the dark water*, or chaos.

If we adopt this identification of the star or constellation Gula with the constellation, or some star in the constellation, Aquarius, it will throw light

[1] Or, rather, "Mercury." See Epping and Strassmaier, *Astronomisches aus Babylon*, p. 112 *et seq.*

[2] Maspero, *Dawn of Civilization*, p. 672, notes 1, 2.

on many of the inscriptions found on statues and other monuments at Telloh (the modern name of the mound which covers the ruins of the ancient city of Lagash).

We find from these inscriptions that the deities especially worshipped at Lagash were not the same as those who held the foremost places contemporaneously in the Accadian, and at a later time in the Babylonian Pantheon. Ningirsu and "his beloved consort," the goddess Bau, received in Lagash the highest honours. On one of the statues of Gudea, "the priestly governor of Lagash," this inscription occurs:[1]—

"To Ningirsu, the powerful warrior of Ellilla [this is dedicated] by Gudea, priestly governor of Lagash, who has constructed the temple of Eninnu, consecrated to Ningirsu.

"For Ningirsu, his lord, he has built the temple of Ekhud, the tower in stages, from the summit of which Ningirsu grants him a happy lot.

"Besides the offerings which Gudea made of his free will to Ningirsu and to the goddess Bau, daughter of Anna, his beloved consort, he has made others to his god Ningiszida.

[1] Evetts, *New Light on the Bible*, p. 162.

"That year he had a block of rare stone brought from the country of Magan; he had it carved into a statue of himself.

"On the day of the beginning of the year, the day of the festival of Bau, on which offerings were made: one calf, one fat sheep, three lambs, six full grown sheep, two rams, seven *pat* of dates, seven *sab* of cream, seven palm buds.

"Such were the offerings made to the goddess Bau in the ancient temple on that day."

Ningirsu, the god—so highly exalted in this and in other inscriptions found in the mounds of Telloh—has been identified with the god Ninib[1] of the Babylonians. Much difference of opinion prevails as to what astronomical ideas were connected by the ancient inhabitants of Mesopotamia with the god Ninib.

Jensen admits that the generally received opinion as to Ninib is that he represents the "southern sun."[2] He, however, contends, with great eagerness, that this is a mistaken opinion, and that Ninib is really the eastern or rising sun. Many of Jensen's arguments against the possibility of Ninib

[1] Maspero, *Dawn of Civilization*, pp. 637, 645.

[2] Jensen, *Die Kosmologie der Babylonier*, p. 460.

representing the southern sun are based on the assumption that the epithet "southern," applied to the sun, denotes the power of the mid-day sun; whereas, in other descriptions of Ninib, he appears as struggling with, though in the end triumphant over, storm, and cloud, and darkness.

The sun in his *daily* course attains the southern meridian at noon, and that may well be described by Jensen as the "alles verzehrenden und versengenden Süd-oder Mittagssonne," but if we think of the sun in his *annual* course, the words "southern sun" may more fitly in an astronomical sense mean the struggling and finally triumphant sun of the winter solstice. And if we so understand the expression, the apparently contradictory references to Ninib are easily explained.

At mid-winter the sun rises and sets more to the south than at any other time of the year; at noon on the day of the winter solstice the sun is forty-seven degrees nearer to the south pole of the heavens than it is at the summer solstice.

If, instead of adopting Jensen's contention, and looking upon Ninib as the eastern rising sun, we revert to the generally held opinion that Ninib was the god of the southern sun, and if we understand the southern sun in its astronomical sense as the winter, or more strictly speaking the mid-winter sun, it will naturally lead us to the conclusion that "the day of the beginning of the year," the day of the festival of Bau, Ningirsu's (=Ninib's) "beloved consort," was held at the time of the winter solstice.

Speaking in round numbers, from 4,000 to 2,000 B.C., the winter solstice took place when the sun was in conjunction with the constellation Aquarius, which constellation, or some one of its stars, was, as has been suggested, called by the Babylonian astronomers, Gula, Gula being another name for Bau.

It is not therefore surprising to find that those rulers of Lagash, whose dates fell between 4,000 and 2,000 B.C., should have so often associated together Ningirsu and Bau; and further, that Gudea, whose rule is placed at about 2,900 B.C., should on "the day of the beginning of the year" have kept high festival in honour of Bau, as the beneficent deity presiding in conjunction with Ningirsu over the revolving years.

The precession of the equinoxes must necessarily in the course of ages introduce confusion into all Zodiacal calendars, and into all ritual and mythological symbolism founded on such calendars. From 2,000 B.C. down to the beginning of our era, the winter solstice took place when the sun was in conjunction with Capricornus, not with Aquarius. In those later days, if the inhabitants of Lagash still celebrated their new year's festival at the winter solstice, Bau (=Gula=Aquarius) could only have laid a traditional claim to preside over it.

In accordance with these astronomical facts, we learn from the teachings of the tablets that the especial reverence paid to Bau=Gula, in the Lagash inscriptions was not extended to her in later times.

As to Ninib, we know that even at Gudea's date in the neighbouring state of Accad, and in later times in Babylon, he did not hold the pre-eminent position accorded to him by the early rulers of Lagash.

This difference in the religious observances of Accad and Lagash regarding Ninib—if we suppose him to be the god of the winter solstice—may also receive an astronomical explanation.

According to the evidence of *The Standard Astrological Work*, the compilation of which is generally attributed to the date 3,800 B.C., and according to the evidence of many other tablets, the year in Accad and afterwards in Babylon began not at the winter solstice, but on the 1st day of Nisan, and Nisan (Acc. Bar zig-gar), the month of "the sacrifice of righteousness," was, as its name suggests, the month during which the sun was in conjunction with the constellation Aries.

At Gudea's date, about 2,900 B.C., the 1st of Nisan, if it was dependent on the sun's entry into Aries, must have fallen about midway between the winter solstice and the spring equinox, and as century succeeded century, the 1st of Nisan must slowly but surely have receded further from the solstice and have approached more and more to the equinoctial point.

In Accad, therefore, neither at Gudea's nor at any later date, did the year begin at the winter solstice, and hence we can understand why in that state, and afterwards in Babylon, Ninib was not as highly honoured as in Lagash, and why he and his consort Bau (=Gula) were not referred to as the deities presiding over the beginning of the year.

In a former number of these *Proceedings*[1] I drew attention to the Accadian calendar. It was there suggested that the choice of the first degree of Aries as the initial point of the Zodiac was originally made when the winter solstice coincided with the sun's entry into that constellation, *i.e.* about 6,000 B.C.

If that suggestion, and the present one concerning the new year's festival in Lagash are accepted, it will be easy to imagine that the Lagash observance betokened a sort of effort to reform the sidereal calendar in use in Accad, and it may be elsewhere.

In Accad the calendar makers clung to the originally instituted *star-mark* for the year, and made it begin with the sun's entry into Aries; therefore by degrees the beginning of their year moved away from the winter solstice, and in the first century B.C. coincided very closely with the spring equinox.

In Lagash, on the contrary, the calendar makers

[1] January 1892, V. p. 13.

clung to the originally established *season* of the year, and made it begin at the winter solstice; therefore by degrees the beginning of their year moved away from the constellation Aries, and in Gudea's time the new year's festival was held in honour of the goddess Bau = Gula = Aquarius.

IV

THE MEDIAN CALENDAR AND THE CONSTELLATION TAURUS

[Reprinted from the *Proceedings of the Society of Biblical Archæology, June* 1897]

IN a former number[1] of these *Proceedings* I contrasted as follows, what I believed to be the calendar of the Accadians with that of the inhabitants of Lagash :—

"In Accad the calendar makers clung to the originally instituted *star-mark* for the year, and made it begin with the sun's entry into [the constellation] Aries; therefore by degrees the beginning of their year moved away from the winter solstice, and in the first century B.C. coincided very closely with the spring equinox.

"In Lagash, on the contrary, the calendar makers clung to the originally established *season*

[1] V. p. 54.

of the year, and made it begin at the winter solstice; therefore by degrees the beginning of their year moved away from the constellation Aries, and in Gudea's time [about 2,900 B.C.] the new year's festival was held in honour of the goddess Bau = Gula = Aquarius."

I now desire to draw attention to the Median calendar, which appears to have differed from that used, as above suggested, in Accad or in Lagash; inasmuch as the beginning of the Median year was not dependent on the sun's entry into the *constellation Aries*, as in Accad; nor was it fixed to the season of the *winter solstice* as in Lagash.

The beginning of the Median year was fixed to the *season of the spring equinox*, and remaining true to that season, followed no star-mark. The great importance, however, of Tauric symbolism in Median art seems to point to the fact that *when the equinoctial year was first established* the spring equinoctial point was in the constellation Taurus. Astronomy teaches us that was the case, speaking in round numbers, from 4,000 to 2,000 B.C.

It is true that we have no documentary proof of the existence of a Median *equinoctial* calendar in the remote past, such as that which we possess in the Babylonian standard astrological works regarding the ancient *sidereal* Accadian calendar. We have, however, among the modern representatives of the Medes, the Persians, a very distinctive calendrical observance, namely, that of the Nowroose, or the festival of the new year; and we have the Persian tradition that the institution of this festival was of fabulous antiquity. I quote from Ker Porter's remarks on this subject:—

"The 21st of March, the impatiently anticipated day of the most joyous festival of Persia, at last arrived. It is called the feast of the Nowroose, or that of the commencement of the new year; and its institution is attributed to the celebrated Jemsheed, who, according to the traditions of the country, and the fragments yet preserved of its early native historians, was the sixth in descent from Noah, and the fourth sovereign of Persia, of the race of Kaiomurs, the grandson of Noah. . . . But to return to the feast of the Nowroose. It is acknowledged to have been celebrated from the earliest ages, in Persia, independent of whatever religions reigned there; whether the simple worship of the One Great Being, or under the successive rites of Magian, Pagan, or Mahomedan institutions." (*Travels*, vol. i. p. 316.)

This equinoctial and solar year, as the writer proceeds to point out, is adhered to by the Persians, though they, being Mahomedans, also celebrate Mahomedan lunar festivals, and for many purposes make use of the Mahomedan lunar year.

It is easy to see how greatly the Persian Nowroose differs from the purely lunar Mahomedan anniversaries—anniversaries which in the course of about thirty-two and a half years necessarily make a complete circuit through the seasons. The difference, though not so marked, which exists between the purely solar Nowroose, and all soli-lunar festivals, such as those of the Babylonians, should also be taken note of. These last, like our Easter, were dependent on the phases of the moon, and were therefore "moveable." The Persian Nowroose, like our Christmas Day, is an "immoveable" festival—fixed to the day of the spring equinox.

Modern tradition concerning the distinctively Persian custom of celebrating the Nowroose would, if it stood alone, furnish very slight grounds on which to found a far-reaching theory; but historical evidence confirms this tradition to a great extent, by teaching us that the Median and Persian worshippers of Ahura Mazda, and of Mithras, certainly under the Sassinide dynasty, and almost with equal certainty under the Achæmenid kings, kept their calendar and celebrated their religious festivals in a manner differing from that of the surrounding nations; their months were not lunar, their years were not soli-lunar but distinctly solar, and the spring equinox was the date to which as closely as possible the beginning of their year was fixed.

In Darmesteter's translation of the *Zend Avesta* the Persian months are treated of in Appendix C, p. 33, and in Appendix D, p. 37, we read of the Persian years:—

"L'année était divisée en quatre saisons, correspondant aux nôtres. Cette division ne paraît guère que dans les textes post-avestéens; mais il y a dans l'Avesta même des traces de son existence ancienne,

La division normale de l'année est, dans l'Avesta, en deux saisons, été et hiver ; l'été, *hama*, qui comprend les sept premiers mois (du 1er Farvardîn au 30 Mihr, soit du 21 mars au 16 octobre). . . . Cette division a une valeur religieuse, non seulement pour le rituel, mais aussi pour les pratiques, qui varient selon la saison."

The worship of the Persian sun-god Mithras was introduced into Rome about the time of the fall of the Republic. How far this worship differed from that taught in the Zoroastrian writings we need not inquire; however changed it may have been, it was evidently derived originally from a Persian or a Median source. The worship of Mithras, in spite of much opposition, gained many followers in Rome. The birthday of the sun-god was kept at the winter solstice, but the great festivities in his honour, "*the mysteries of Mithras*," were as a rule celebrated at the season of the spring equinox,[1]

[1] Cumont, in the first volume of his *Monuments figurés relatifs aux mystères de Mithra*, p. 326, having spoken of the solstitial festival in honour of the birthday of the god, observes as follows : " Nous avons certaines raisons de croire que les équinoxes étaient aussi des jours fériés où l'on inaugurait par quelque salutation le retour des Saisons divinisées. Les initiations avaient lieu de préférence vers le début du printemps, en mars ou en avril. . ."

and were famous even among Roman festivals. Let us now turn our attention to the Tauric symbolism so closely connected with Mithraic observances in Rome.

A writer in the *Athenæum* thus describes a Roman Mithræum:[1] "Discovery was made during some excavations at Ostia of a handsome house containing among its various rooms a *mithræum*. . . . Into the kitchen opens a narrow and tortuous passage, from which by a small half-concealed staircase the *mithræum* is reached; . . . it is quadrangular and regular in shape, as is usually the case in buildings of the kind. Almost the whole length of the two lateral walls run two seats, and on the side opposite the door is seen a little elevation, which served as the place for the usual statue of Mithras in the act of thrusting his dagger into the neck of the mystic Bull. A very singular peculiarity of this little Ostian *mithræum* is that it is entirely covered with mosaics—pavements, seats, and walls alike. The various figures and the symbols are splendidly drawn, and all executed in black *tesseræ* on a white ground. Upon each side of the seats, turned to the entrance door, is figured a genius bearing a lamp, that is, the genius of the

[1] *Athenæum*, 1886, October 30 and November 6.

spring equinox, with the face raised, and that of the autumn equinox, with the face cast down. . . . It is known, in fact, that the whole myth of Mithras is related to the phases of the sun . . . hence are represented in the ground below the seats all the twelve signs of the zodiac, by means of the usual symbols, but each accompanied by a large star."

In the many sculptures of the Mithras group similar to that above described, which have been so well figured in Lajard's *Culte de Mithras*, various heavenly bodies are represented. The Scorpion (the constellation Scorpio of the Zodiac opposed to Taurus) joins with Mithras in his attack upon the Bull, and always the genii of the spring and autumn equinoxes are present in joyous and mournful attitudes.

In looking at these plates the conviction is clearly forced upon our minds that the Bull so persistently, and, it may be added, so serenely, slain by Mithras in these Roman representations, is the Zodiacal Bull, overcome, and as it were destroyed or banished from heaven, in the daytime by the sun-god, and at night by Scorpio, the constellation in opposition. With almost equal conviction we arrive at the conclusion that this triumph of Mithras was associated traditionally—in Roman days it could only have been traditionally—with the occurrence, at a remote date, of the spring equinox during the time that the sun was in conjunction with the constellation Taurus.

In the ruins of Persepolis, ruins of buildings designed, erected, and decorated by the worshippers of the supreme God Ahura Mazda, and of his friend and representative Mithras, Tauric symbolism abounds. We do not amongst these ruins find portrayals of Mithras as a youth wearing a Phrygian cap, and "thrusting his dagger into the neck of the mystic Bull," but again and again, in the bas-reliefs adorning the walls, we do find a colossal being thrusting his dagger into the body of a still more "mystic" creature than the Bull of the Roman sculptures—a creature combining in one instance at least[1] the attributes of Bull, Lion, Scorpion, and Eagle, and frequently those of two or more of these animals.

Perrot and Chipiez have supposed this constantly repeated scene to represent imaginary

[1] See Plate IV.

PLATE IV.

Persépolis. Combat du roi et du griffon. Palais n° 3.
Perrot et Chipiez. *Histoire de l'Art dans l'Antiquité*,
Tome v. opposite page 547.

[*To face p.* 64.

contests between the reigning monarch and all possible or impossible monsters, but a very different impression was produced on the mind of Ker Porter by these same bas-reliefs; and though he did not adopt a purely astronomic theory to explain them, he was firmly convinced that the combat depicted was not one waged between an ordinary human being and an ordinary or extraordinary animal, but that it was a symbolical representation of the combat constantly carried on by Ormuzd (Ahura Mazda), and by his representative Mithras, against the powers of evil and darkness.[1]

With the astronomic clue to Persian symbolism

[1] "The man who contends with the animals . . . is represented as a person of a singularly dignified mien, clad in long draperied robes, but with the arms perfectly bare. His hair, which is full and curled, is bound with a circlet or low diadem; and his sweeping pointed beard is curled at different heights, in the style that was worn by majesty alone. . . . The calmness of his air, contrasted with the firmness with which he grasps the animals, and strikes to his aim, gives a certainty to his object, and a sublimity to his figure, beyond anything that would have been in the power of more elaborate action or ornament to effect. From the unchanged appearance of the hero, his unvaried mode of attack, its success, and the unaltered style of opposition adopted by every one of the animals in the contest, I can have no doubt that they all mean different achievements towards one great aim. . . ."—Ker Porter's *Travels*, vol. i. p. 672.

put into our hands by the Roman sculptures, of which mention has been made, and by a study of the researches of Lajard, it is not difficult to recognize in the composite animals represented on the bas-reliefs allusions not only to the Zodiacal Bull, traditionally associated with the spring equinox, but also to three other constellations which at the same date of the world's history (namely, from 4,000 to 2,000 B.C.) marked more or less accurately the remaining colures, *i.e.* the Lion, the Scorpion, and the Eagle.

The constellations of the Lion and the Scorpion, there can be no doubt, were appropriate star marks for the summer and autumn seasons, when the spring equinoctial point was in the Bull,[1] but as regards the Eagle it must be admitted that though it adjoins the Zodiacal Aquarius (the constellation in which the winter solstitial point was then situated), yet its principal stars lie considerably to the north and west of that constellation.

A reason for the substitution of the Eagle (Aquila) for the Zodiacal Water-man or Water-jar

[1] The solstitial and equinoctial colures were situated, speaking in round numbers, for 2,000 years in the constellations Taurus, Leo, Scorpio, and Aquarius.

(Aquarius or Amphora) may, however, be found in the fact of the very great brilliancy of the star Altair in the Eagle. It is a star of the first magnitude. In the Water-man there is no star above the third. The Persians, we are told, had a tradition that four brilliant stars marked the four cardinal points (*i.e.* the colures). In Taurus, Leo, and Scorpio we find stars of the first magnitude: there was therefore no temptation for Mithraic calendar makers and mythologists to seek for an extra-Zodiacal star to mark and represent the spring, summer, or autumn seasons; but for the winter solstice the only stars of the first magnitude within at all suitable distance were Aquila, to the north-west, or Fomalhaut to the south of Aquarius. For a nation dwelling as far to the north as the Medians are supposed to have done, Fomalhaut (when the winter solstice was in Aquarius very far to the south of the equator) would have been rarely visible. The choice by a Median astronomer and symbolic artist in search of a very brilliant star mark for the solstice would therefore have been restricted to the constellation of the Eagle, containing the conspicuous Altair, a star of the first magnitude.

The very constant association, not only in Persian and Median, but also in the mythologic art of other nations, of the Lion and the Eagle, seems to confirm the view here put forward, *i.e.* that the constellations of Leo and Aquila rather than of Leo and Aquarius were sometimes chosen to symbolise the summer and winter solstices.

The Griffin, a fabulous animal sacred to the sun, composed of a *Lion* and an *Eagle*, is a well-known figure in ancient classic art.

In Babylonian and Assyrian sculptured and glyptic art Merodach is often represented as in conflict with a Griffin. Merodach has been claimed by Jensen and other writers as a personification of the sun of the spring equinox. The for ever recurring triumph of spring over winter is probably figured in Merodach's triumph over the Griffin.

The association of Eagle and Lion is to be noticed in the arms of the city of Lagash; they were "a double-headed Eagle standing on a Lion passant or on two demi-lions placed back to back."[1] In Lagash, as was pointed out in a former paper, the new year's festival appears to have been held at the

[1] Maspero, *Dawn of Civilization*, p. 604.

winter solstice : such a supposition would furnish an astronomical interpretation for the arms of Lagash.[1]

Mythological references to the Eagle alone are also to be met with which point to the Celestial Eagle (Aquila) marking the winter solstice in lieu of the constellation Aquarius, as for instance the Babylonian legend of the ambitious storm-bird, Zu,[2] who stole the tablets of destiny, and thus sought to vie in power with "the great gods." Here we may find allusions to the substitution (deemed by some,

[1] In this connexion the following passage from Sayce's *Hibbert Lectures*, p. 261, is interesting :—

A text copied for Assur-banipal, from a tablet originally written at Babylon, contains part of a hymn which had to be recited "in the presence of Bel-Merodach . . . in the beginning of Nisan,"—

". . . . O Zamama,
Why dost thou not take thy seat?
Bahu, the Queen of Kis, has not cried to thee."

He adds in a note that Zamama was the Sun-god of Kis, and was consequently identified with Adar by the mythologists. On a contract-stone he is symbolized by an eagle, which is said to be "the image of the southern sun of Kis."

It was claimed in a former paper (Feb. 1896) that "*the Southern sun*" was "*the sun of the winter solstice*," and that Gula (= Bahu) was the name of the constellation, or of some stars in the constellation Aquarius (V. p. 50). In these lines Bahu, as I have supposed, Aquarius, and Zamama, symbolised by the *Eagle, the image of the Southern sun or winter solstice*, are closely associated.

[2] Maspero, *Dawn of Civilization*, p. 666.

no doubt, unauthorized) of an extra-Zodiacal for a Zodiacal constellation.

Again, in Grecian mythology the Eagle is sent by Zeus to carry Ganymede up to heaven, and in Grecian astronomy Ganymede is placed in the constellation Aquarius. It does not therefore seem unreasonable to suppose that the Eagle associated in the Persepolitan bas-reliefs with the Lion, the Bull, and the Scorpion (as at Plate IV.), is the constellational Eagle, symbolizing the winter solstice, and that the compound animal is emblematic of the four seasons of the year, and also, it may be, of the four quarters of the world.

If to the composite monster of the bas-reliefs we ascribe an astronomic motive, we shall be ready to grant the same to other Tauric symbolisms prominent in the Persepolitan ruins.

With full conviction we shall recognize in the demi-bulls which crowned the columns in Persepolis and Susa representations of the demi-bull of the Zodiac. The resemblance is so striking that words are scarcely required to point it out when once the outlines of the two figures have been compared (Plate V.). In the spirited description of these

PLATE V.

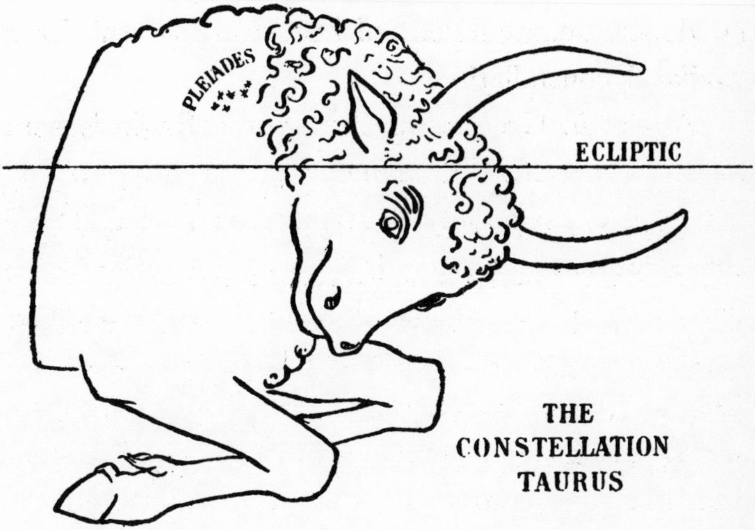

THE CONSTELLATION TAURUS

CAPITAL FROM SUSA

[*To face p.* 70.

capitals, quoted here from Perrot and Chipiez,[1] are some lines, marked with italics, which might be applied with exactness to the demi-bulls of the Zodiac.

"On ne saurait cependant ne point admirer le grand goût et l'art ingénieux avec lequel, dans ses bustes de taureau, il [l'artiste perse] a plié la forme vivante au nécessités de la décoration architecturale. Il a su la simplifier sans lui enlever l'accent de la vie; les traits caractéristiques de l'espèce sur laquelle s'est porté son choix restent franchement accusés, quoique les menus détails soient éliminés; ils auraient risqué de distraire et de troubler le regard. Les poils de la nuque et du dos, de l'épaule, des fanons, et des flancs sont réunis en masses d'un ferme contour, auquelles la frisure des boucles dont elles se composent donne un relief plus vigoureux; en même temps le collier qui pend au col, orné de rosaces et d'un riche fleuron qui tombe sur la poitrine, écarte toute idée de réalité; ce sont là des êtres sacrés et presque divins, que l'imagination de l'artiste a comme créés à nouveau et modelés à son gré pour les adapter à la fonction qu'elle leur donnait à remplir. Cependant, tout placé qu'il soit en dehors des conditions de la nature, l'animal n'a

[1] *Histoire de l'Art dans l'antiquité*, Perse, p. 519.

pas perdu sa physionomie propre. Dans le mouvement de *la tête, légèrement inclinée en avant et sur la côté*, on sent la force indomptée qui anime ce corps ample et puissant. Hardiment indiquées, la construction et la musculature des *membres inférieurs, repliés sous le ventre*, laissent deviner de quel élan le taureau se lèverait et se dresserait en pied, s'il venait à se lasser de son éternel repos. J'en ai fait plusieurs fois l'expérience au Louvre, devant la partie de chapiteau colossal que notre musée doit à M. Dieulafoy : parmi les visiteurs qui se pressaient dans cette salle, parmi ceux mêmes qui semblaient le moins préparés à éprouver ce genre d'impressions, il n'en est pas un qui n'ait subi le charme, qui de manière ou d'autre, n'ait rendu hommage à la noblesse et à l'étrange beauté de ce type singulier."

For the exquisite columns crowned by these Tauric capitals the same writers have claimed a distinctively Median origin. This claim they sustain at great length, and with much architectural learning. They show that in their proportions, and in every detail of their ornamentation, the Persepolitan differed from the Ninevite, Grecian, or Egyptian column. They also point out that nowhere except at Persepolis and at Susa is the demi-bull of the capital to be met with; and yet they express the opinion that this feature, so far as is known proper to Persia, was mainly derived from, or helped at least by, the models of Assyria.

Very close resemblances can indeed be traced in Medo-Persian to Assyrian art, and as the Medo-Persian buildings, whose ruins are at Persepolis and Susa, were erected certainly at a later date than the palaces of the Assyrian kings discovered on the site of Nineveh, it is natural to attribute, as Perrot and Chipiez, and nearly all writers on the subject attribute, such resemblances to imitations of Assyrian art and symbolism on the part of the Medo-Persians.

There are, however, some considerations which make it difficult to adopt this view. In the first place, the symbolism supposed to have been copied by the Medo-Persians was religious symbolism, and the religion of the Aryan Medo-Persians was very different from that of the Semitic Assyrians.

The Achæmenid kings who built their palaces at Persepolis claimed constantly that they were worshippers of the one great Lord Ahura Mazda, of whom Mithras was the friend and representative. That these kings should have adopted from the polytheistic Assyrians not only the Tauric symbolism above described, but also, as it is suggested, the emblem of their one great Lord Ahura Mazda from that of Assur (see Plate VI. figs. 1, 2, 3), would in itself be strange, but that they should have done so when Assur and all his followers had been utterly vanquished by the victorious worshippers of Ahura Mazda, seems still more improbable.

From the state in which the ruins of Nineveh were when discovered by Layard it is easy to see that, from the very day of the sacking of the city, it had for the most part been left just as it fell. It may have been rifled of its material wealth, but its literary and artistic treasures were left uncared for and undesired. A few hundred years later the very site of Nineveh was unknown.

The great city would not have been treated with such neglect had the Medo-Persian artists turned to it for inspiration and for themes of symbolic art with which to decorate the palaces of Persepolis,

PLATE VI.

FIG. 1.

The Assyrian god Assur.

FIG. 2.

The Assyrian god Assur.

PLATE VI.

FIG. 3.

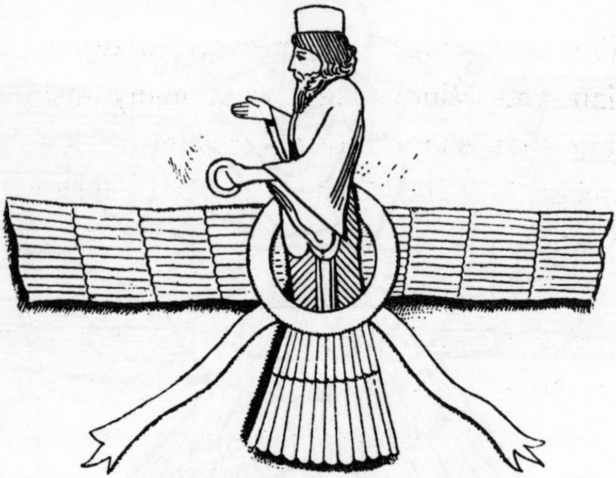

The Median god Ahura Mazda.

FIG. 4.

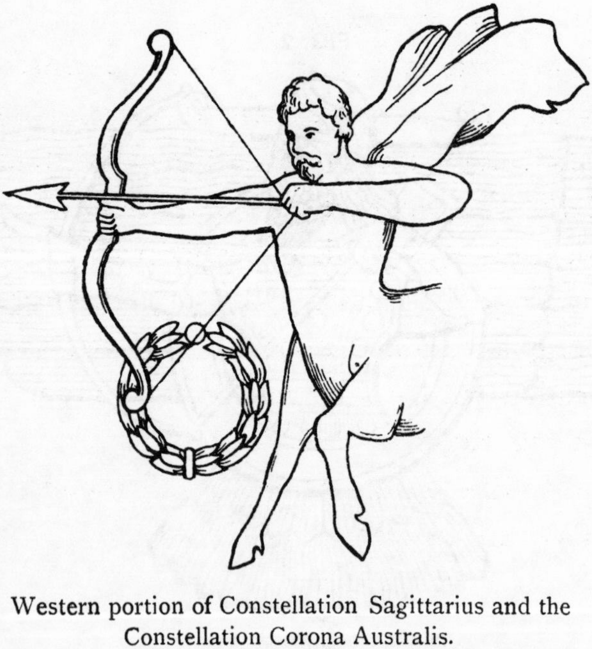

Western portion of Constellation Sagittarius and the Constellation Corona Australis.

The resemblance, however, between Medo-Persian and Ninevite art is in many instances so striking that some way of accounting for it must be sought, and those who are dissatisfied with one explanation will naturally look about to find some alternative suggestion.

The alternative suggestion I would now propose is that *the progenitors of the Assyrians at an early period of the world's history borrowed Tauric and other religious symbolisms from the ancestors of the Medes.*

In support of this theory the following considerations are put forward:

Tauric symbolism, if it is at all astronomic, points us back to a very remote date for its first institution, to a date considerably earlier than that at which the existence of the Assyrian people as an independent nation is generally put. The symbolism already discussed must, at the latest, have been originated about 2,000 B.C. Of the Assyrians as a nation we have no monumental proof earlier than 1,700 B.C.

But further, in the symbol of Ahura and Assur, I believe an astronomic reference may be traced to the position of the colures amongst the constellations, a reference which points us back not merely to a date between 4,000 and 2,000 B.C., but rather, and with curious precision, to the furthest limit of the time mentioned, namely to 4,000 B.C.

To penetrate into the meaning of this symbol of Ahura we must study both the Median and Assyrian representations of the figure presiding over the winged disc, and we may also seek for further light to be thrown upon it by other references in Assyrian art to the god Assur.

Ahura presiding over the winged circle holds in his hand a ring or crown; Assur in some examples is similarly furnished; but more often he appears armed with bow and arrows. In this figure, variously equipped, I believe that the heavenly Archer, the Zodiacal Sagittarius (Plate VI. fig. 4), is to be recognized—Sagittarius, the constellation in which the autumnal equinoctial point was situated, speaking in round numbers, from 6,000 to 4,000 B.C.

The fact that a crown or wreath or ring often replaces the bow and arrows in the hand of Ahura and of Assur might at first sight make us doubtful as to the connexion of the figure with the constellation Sagittarius, but a glance at the celestial globe will rather make this fact tell in favour of the astronomical suggestion here made: for there we find close to the hand of the Archer the ancient Ptolemaic constellation Corona Australis (the Southern Crown), actually incorporated with the Zodiacal constellation Sagittarius.

Not only do Assur's bow and crown remind us of Sagittarius, but his horned tiara, resembling so closely that worn by the man-headed Assyrian bulls, inclines us to look for some astronomic and Tauric allusion in this Assyrian and Median symbol.

True it is that, speaking generally, Gemini and not Taurus is the constellation of the Zodiac opposed to Sagittarius, but owing to the irregularity in the shape and size of the portions assigned in the ecliptic to the Zodiacal constellations, the extreme western degrees of Sagittarius are opposed to the extreme eastern degrees of Taurus. Therefore about 4,000 B.C. the equinoctial colure passed through the constellations of the Archer and the Bull.

In the Assyrian Standard (depicted in Layard's *Monuments of Nineveh*, Plate XXII.)

we see the figure of an Archer above that of a galloping Bull, and in another Assyrian

Standard, that of Sargon II., we find not only

PLATE VII.

Standard of Sargon II., King of Assyria, 722-705 B.C.

Perrot et Chipiez. *Histoire de l'Art dans l'Antiquité*, Tome v. opposite page 508.

[*To face p.* 79.

the Archer and the Bull, the two constellations which 4,000 B.C. marked the *equinoctial* colure, but we may also clearly trace a reference to the two constellations which at the same date marked the *solstitial* colure, namely, those of the Lion and the Water-man (Plate VII.).

Here the *Archer* dominates over a circle in which symmetrically duplicated *Bulls* appear, and duplicated *Lions'* heads emerge out of what appears to be a hollow vessel resembling a *water jar;* the wavy lines that traverse the disc suggest streams that unitedly pour their waters into this jar. Below the jar again are to be seen halved and doubled heads, partly Lion and partly Bull.

This Standard of Assur may (like the Persepolitan monster earlier described) be considered as an astronomic monogram representing the four constellations which marked the four seasons of the year, and the four quarters of the earth.

The monogram of the Standard refers us back, however, to an earlier date for its origin than does the monogram of the composite animal in the Persepolitan bas-relief, for in the Standard the Archer is opposed to the Bull, in the bas-relief the Scorpion takes the place of the Archer, and the Eagle takes the place of the Water-man.

The precession of the equinoxes advances from east to west amongst the stars. Therefore the Scorpion marked the colure at a later date than did the Archer. The Eagle, as has already been pointed out, is considerably to the west of Aquarius, and could scarcely have been chosen as a substitute for that constellation when the colure was in its extreme eastern degrees.

At Plate VIII. is given the position of the colures at 4,000 B.C.; not much earlier or much later than this date can we place the *origin* of the symbolism in the Standard shown at Plate VII. Earlier *not* Leo and Aquarius, but Virgo and Pisces, would have marked the solstitial colure. Later *not* Sagittarius, but Scorpio, would have in opposition to Taurus marked the equinoctial colure.

At this date, 4,000 B.C., suggested with such curious accuracy by this Assyrian Standard, we have absolutely no trace of the existence of the *Semitic nation of the Assyrians* in Northern Mesopotamia. In Babylonia two hundred years later the Semitic Sargon I. ruled at Accad. In the

PLATE VIII.

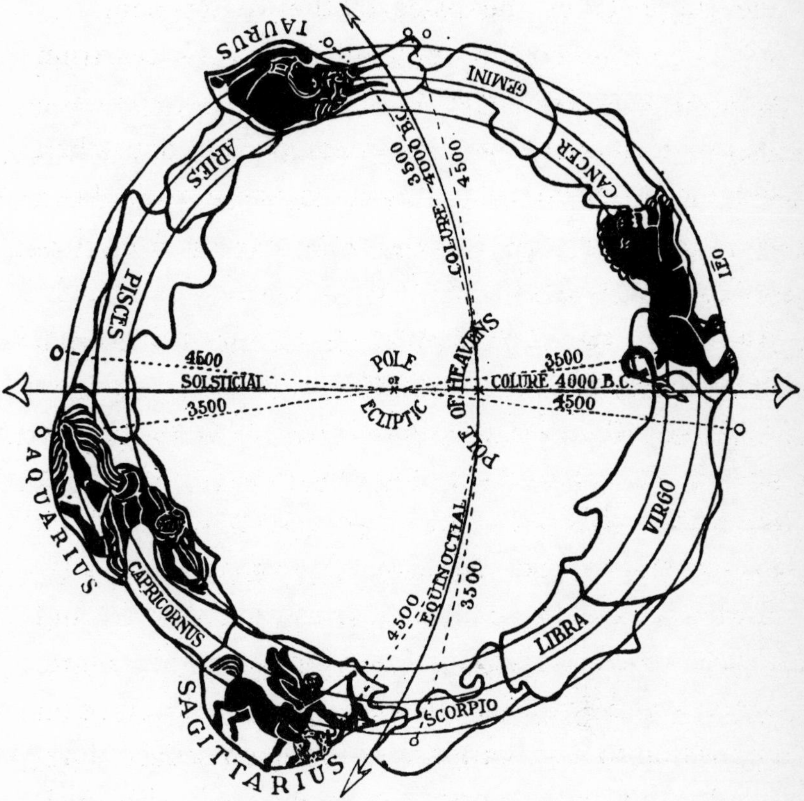

Position of Colures amongst the Constellations at the dates 4,500–4,000 and 3,500 B.C.

[*To face p.* 80.

astrological work drawn up, if not for Sargon yet, as we may judge from internal evidence, for some king of Accad, no mention is made of the Assyrian nation.

The Phœnicians, the Hittites, the Kings of Gutium, and the "Umman Manda" are then the dreaded foes of Accad. Of the Manda we read as follows: "The Umman Manda comes and governs the land. The mercy seats of the great gods are taken away. Bel goes to Elam."

Professor Sayce is opposed to the view that the Manda are necessarily identical with the Medes; but he admits that Herodotus, following the authority of Medo-Persian writers, claimed as Median the victories of the Manda.[1]

If now on the authority of Herodotus and the Medo-Persian writers we assume, at least as a possibility, that these Manda were Medes, we should expect to find them worshippers of Ahura Mazda. Ahura, it is on all hands admitted, is the Iranian form of the Vedic Asura, just as Mithras is the Iranian form of the Vedic Mitra. At whatever date the separation between Iranian and Vedic

[1] *Proceedings*, vol. xviii. Part vi. pp. 176, 177.

Aryans took place, the worship of Ahura (still probably under the form Asura) must have existed amongst the Iranians; indeed, many have supposed that the monotheistic reform which placed one great Ahura or Asura above all other Asuras, and above the Devas, occasioned the separation of these two great Aryan races.

It is for the Lord Ahura, called, as here supposed, Asura, in early times, by the Aryan Manda, that I would claim the astronomical symbol of the Archer presiding over the circle of the ecliptic, or, in other words, over the circle of the year, and of a year beginning at the spring equinox—a year, as has already been pointed out, distinctively Median.

According then to this supposition, a powerful Median race was established in the vicinity of Babylonia early in the fourth millennium B.C.—a race who worshipped one great Lord, first under the name of Asura, afterwards under that of Ahura.

It is for these Aryan Manda or Medes that I would claim, at the date of 4,000 B.C., the original conception of the astronomic monogram in which so plainly may be read an allusion to the four constellations of the Zodiac, which at that date marked the four seasons and the four cardinal points, *i.e.* Sagittarius and Taurus, Aquarius and Leo. This monogram was used as a Standard thousands of years later by the Semitic Assyrians.

To the Manda or Medes, also, I would, as has been suggested, attribute the first imagining of the astronomic emblem common to Ahura and Assur—that of the divine Being presiding over the circle of the ecliptic.

Berosus mentions a Median dynasty as having reigned in Babylon for one or two hundred years. Let us now suppose that the Manda for more than a thousand years held power in *Northern* Mesopotamia, but that at last the tide of conquest turned, and after many struggles with the Semites in the south the Aryans were finally driven from the land now known as Assyria, and a Semite race firmly settled in the regions from whence in Sargon's time the Umman Manda had threatened the inhabitants of the Kingdom of Accad. That this was the case about 2,200 B.C. may perhaps be gathered from the monuments of Ḫammurabi, the

Semitic king of Babylon, for he refers in his letters to his troops in *Assyria*, and in a lately discovered inscription of this king he speaks of restoring to the city of *Assur* its propitious genie, and of honouring Istar in the city of Nineveh.

To account for the existence of the Assyrian nation, their close resemblance in language and race to the ruling Semitic class in Babylon, and yet to explain the great difference in the religion of these two peoples, has always been a difficulty.

The Assyrians worshipped, and worshipped with enthusiasm, all the Babylonian gods; but high above the whole Babylonian Pantheon they placed as their supreme and great Lord Assur—Assur whose very name is not to be met with in Babylonian mythology. This difficulty I would explain in the following manner.

When the Medes had, by Ḫammurabi or his successors, been driven out of Northern Mesopotamia, they were replaced by Semitic settlers who (like the settlers sent into Samaria more than a thousand years later by a king of Assyria) adopted, to a certain extent, the religion of the nation whom they had dispossessed. In 2 Kings xvii. we read that in this parallel instance "the king of Assyria brought men from Babylon, and from Cuthah, and from Ava, and from Hamath, and from Sepharvaim, and placed them in the cities of Samaria instead of the children of Israel: and they possessed Samaria, and dwelt in the cities thereof." Later in the same chapter we read that in order to appease, as they believed, the wrath of the "God of the land," these idolatrous settlers, retaining in full the worship of all their own gods, added to it a worship of the Lord of the dispossessed Israelites.

I would suppose then that the polytheistic Semites, who in Ḫammurabi's time were settled in Northern Mesopotamia. had acted in a similar manner. Coming into a region where for nearly 2,000 years the monotheistic Medes or Manda had been established, they, to avert the wrath of the *god of the land*, adopted to a certain extent his worship. In fact, like the Samaritans, "they feared the Lord [Asura], and served their own gods."

This explanation of the difference in religion between the Babylonians and the Assyrians seems to yield also an explanation of the resemblances between the Assyrian and Median religions, or rather of the resemblances between the religious art of the two peoples; and thus we return to the problem proposed for discussion earlier in this Paper, namely, the inadequacy of the generally held opinion which accounts for the resemblances in Persepolitan and Ninevite symbolic art by supposing that the Medes borrowed from the Assyrians.

In support of the alternative suggestion put forward at p. 75, that *the progenitors of the Assyrians at an early period of the world's history borrowed Tauric and other religious symbolisms from the ancestors of the Medes*, I would claim that the Assyrians borrowed not only religious symbolisms, but even the very name of their god Assur from the Medes. For I look upon Assur as a "loan word" adopted from the Aryan Asura.

To the Medes or Manda, who were, as has been argued, in power in Northern Mesopotamia about 4,000 B.C., I have attributed the origin of the astronomic Assyrian and Ahurian emblem. To them, on the same grounds, I attribute the first imagining of the astronomic Assyrian Standard, and the devising of the man-headed and winged monsters so well known as "Assyrian Bulls"; and to them I would, with full conviction, leave the honour of having invented, and not borrowed, the idea of the magnificent Tauric capitals that crowned the columns of Persepolis and Susa.

To all these conclusions I have been led by a consideration of the distinctively equinoctial character of the Median calendar, taken in connexion with the importance given in Median art to the constellation Taurus.

V

ASTRONOMY IN THE RIG VEDA

[Reprinted from the Report of the *Actes* of the Twelfth Oriental Congress held at Rome]

NOT much more than a hundred years ago the Sanscrit language began to yield to the study of Europeans some of its literary treasures. Almost on the moment, a controversy arose as to the antiquity of the science of astronomy in India; for scholars were amazed to find in this already long dead language many learned astronomical treatises, besides complete instructions for calculating, year by year, the Hindu calendar, as also for calculating horoscopes.

Some then proclaimed the wonderful facts revealed, and extolled the antiquity and accuracy of this Indian science, while others, noticing the many points of resemblance between European and Indian methods, supposed, and warmly advocated the opinion, that much of the astronomy contained in Sanscrit works had been borrowed from the Greeks.

Sir William Jones was amongst the first to enter the lists against this Grecian theory; and he thus throws down his glove in defence of the antiquity and originality of the science of astronomy in India.

"I engage to support an opinion (which the learned and industrious M. Montucla seems to treat with extreme contempt) that the *Indian* division of the Zodiack was not borrowed from the *Greeks* or *Arabs*, but, having been known in this country (India) for time immemorial, and being the same in part with that used by other nations of the old *Hindu* race, was probably invented by the first progenitors of that race before their dispersion."[1]

Since Sir William Jones wrote this challenge, and supported it with whatever linguistic and scientific resources were at his command, volumes of heated controversy by many authors have been devoted to the same subject.

[1] *On the Antiquity of the Indian Zodiack. Complete Works*, vol. i. p. 333.

Just at present, however, an almost indifferent calmness has taken the place of the excited interest formerly manifested. The majority of scholars, both European and Indian, appear to have accepted, as an axiom, the opinion that much of Indian astronomy, and certainly the Indian acquaintance with the twelve-fold division of the Zodiac, is to be attributed to Grecian influence.

A minority of writers still hold the view advocated by Sir William Jones about a hundred years ago, and thus reiterated by Burgess (the translator of the Indian standard astronomical work the *Sûrya-Siddhânta*) in 1860. "The use of this (twelve-fold) division, and the present names of the signs, can be proved to have existed in India at as early a period as in any other country."[1]

The minority who hold this view are so few at present that, as has been said, the majority rest in their opposed opinion in all the calmness of conviction.

I will now as briefly as possible state the chief arguments put forward, for and against, this conviction.

[1] *Journal of the American Oriental Society*, vol. vi. p. 477.

I. In favour of the comparatively late introduction into India of the twelve-fold division of the Zodiac, it is contended that the divisions of the Indian Solar Zodiac so closely resemble those of the Grecian (the Zodiac which we to this day depict on celestial globes), that it is not possible to believe that two nations or two sets of astronomers could independently of each other have imagined the same fanciful and apparently inconsequent series.

History does not tell of communication between Greece and India, sufficient to account for this similarity of astronomical method, till after the date of Alexander's conquest—about 300 B.C. The Greeks could not at that late date have first become acquainted with the figures of the Zodiac, for in Grecian literature of a much earlier age the figures of the Zodiac and other constellations are alluded to as already perfectly well known. As the Greeks therefore could not have learnt all their astronomic lore from the Indians, the Indians must have learnt theirs from the Greeks at some date later than Alexander's Eastern conquests.

A corroboration of this opinion is drawn from

the consideration that, in the most ancient Sanscrit work in existence—the purely Indian Rig Veda, containing no Grecian taint—the twelve-fold divisions of the Zodiac appear to be unknown. This opinion as to the Rashis or constellations of the Solar Zodiac is so generally adopted, that the age of any Sanscrit work in which mention of these Rashis occurs is at once—no matter what its claims to antiquity may be—set down as not earlier than the comparatively modern date of 300 B.C.

II. As regards the Indian Lunar Zodiac. The Indians make use at present for calendrical purposes, not only of the twelve-fold Solar Zodiac, they have also a series of 27 Nakshatras, or Lunar mansions (this is for convenience sake designated by European writers as the Lunar Zodiac). It is admitted on all hands that the Nakshatra series was not derived from Grecian sources. But it is contended that the fixation of the initial point of this Lunar Zodiac (a point at the end of Revatī and the beginning of Aswinī, 10 degrees west of the first point of our constellation Aries) was due to an astronomical reform of the Hindu calendar, probably carried out under Grecian auspices at a date not much earlier than 600 A.D. A very clear statement of this opinion is thus given by Whitney (the editor of Burgess' translation of the *Sûrya Siddhânta*) :—

"The initial point of the fixed Hindu sphere from which longitudes are reckoned, and at which the planetary motions are held by all schools of Hindu astronomy to have commenced at the creation, is the end of the asterism Revatî, or the beginning of Açvinî. Its situation is most nearly marked by that of the principal star of Revatî . . . that star is by all authorities identified with ζ Piscium, of which the longitude at present, as reckoned by us, from the Vernal Equinox, is $17° 54'$. Making due allowance for the precession (of the equinoxes), we find that it coincided in position with the vernal equinox, not far from the middle of the sixth century, or about A.D. 570. *As such coincidence was the occasion of the point being fixed upon as the beginning of the sphere*, the time of its occurrence marks approximately the era of the fixation of the sphere, and of the commencement of the history of modern Hindu astronomy."[1]

[1] *Journal of the American Oriental Society*, vol. vi. p. 158.

In further corroboration of this view—deduced from the astronomical supposition (to which I have drawn attention by italics) put forward in this extract—ancient Sanscrit literature is appealed to. Hymns and lists referring to the Nakshatras are to be met with in the Yajur and Atharva Vedas, in which Krittikā, now the third Nakshatra, holds the first place.

The Nakshatra Krittikā contains the group of stars known to us as the Pleiades. The most brilliant stars in the Nakshatra Aswinī are the two stars in the head of the constellation Aries (the Ram), known to astronomers as α and β Arietis.

The vernal equinoctial point coincided about 2,000 B.C. with the constellation Krittikā. It is considered to be most probable that on account of this coincidence, at the early date when the hymns and list in question were composed, Krittikā was chosen as the leader of the Nakshatra series, and hence a similar reason for the later choice of Aswinī as leader relegates it to a date not much earlier than 570 A.D.

These very briefly, as far as I have been able

to gather them, are the chief arguments in favour of—

(1) The Grecian introduction of the twelve-fold Zodiac into India about 300 B.C.

(2) The date of 570 A.D. for the fixation of the initial point of the Indian Zodiacs, and for the commencement of the history of Indian astronomy.

These propositions are based on cogent reasonings, and are maintained by very high authorities. The opponents of the modern theory have brought and bring forward the following considerations:—

"The *Bráhmans* were always too proud to borrow their science from the *Greeks*, *Arabs*, *Moguls*, or any nation of *Mléchch'has*, as they call those who are ignorant of the *Védas*, and have not studied the language of the Gods; they have often quoted to me (Sir William Jones) the fragment of an old verse, which they now use proverbially (*na níchò yavanátparah*), or, '*no base creature can be lower than a Yavan*,' by which name they formerly meant an *Ionian* or *Greek*, and now mean a *Mogul*."[1]

[1] Sir William Jones, *The Antiquity of the Indian Zodiack*, *Complete Works*, vol. i. p. 345.

Again the same writer points out that the resemblance between the Indian and the Greek Zodiac is—

"not more extraordinary than that, which has often been observed between our *Gothick* days of the week and those of the *Hindus*, which are dedicated to the same luminaries, and (what is yet more singular) revolve in the same order: *Ravi*, the Sun; *Sóma*, the Moon; *Mangala*, Tuisco; *Budha*, Woden; *Vrihaspati*, Thor; *Sucra*, Freya; *Sani*, Sater; yet no man ever imagined that the *Indians* borrowed so remarkable an arrangement from the *Goths* or *Germans*."

These considerations put forward by Sir William Jones are further emphasized by the reflection that not only does the Grecian theory entail the improbability of the proud and jealous Brahmins adopting into their science and their mythology the teachings of foreigners; but that it also entails the greater improbability of the two rival Hindu sects, Brahmins and Buddhists, having at the same date and with equal enthusiasm adopted into their science and religious symbolism and calendars the same innovations.

Again the opinion of the Greek writers at the beginning of our era may be quoted as showing the high estimation in which, at that time of the world, Indian astronomy was held: as for instance in the life of Apollonius of Tyana (written about 210 A.D. by Philostratus), the wisdom and learning of Apollonius are set high above those of all his contemporaries; but from the sages of India he is represented as learning many things, especially matters of astronomy.[1]

This high opinion held by Greeks in regard to Indian astronomy may be contrasted with the very moderate praise bestowed on the Grecian science by Garga, a Hindu writer of, it is supposed, the first century B.C. He says:—

"The Yavanas (Greeks) are Mlechchas (non-Hindus, or barbarians), but amongst them this science (astronomy) is well established. Therefore they are honoured as Rishis (saints); how much more then an astronomer who is a Brahman?"[2]

Somewhat to the same effect speaks a Hindu author of a later date, Varāhamihira, who wrote

[1] *Apollonius of Tyana*, Book iii. chapter 13.

[2] Romesh Chunder Dutt, *Ancient India*, p. 136.

an astronomical dissertation treating of five different works known to him on the science of astronomy. He says :—

"There are the following Siddhântas: The Pauliśa, the Romaka, the Vâsistha, the Saura, and the Paitámaha. Out of these five, the first two (the Pauliśa and Romaka, which appear to have been European treatises) have been explained by Lâṭadeva. The Siddhânta made by Pauliśa is accurate, near to it stands the Siddhánta proclaimed by Romaka; more accurate is the Sávitra (Saura)[1] (*Sūrya Siddhānta*, the *Hindu* standard work); the two remaining ones are far from the truth."[2]

This moderate, and, as it reads, judicial opinion of Varāhamihira, touching the superiority of the native *Sūrya Siddhānta* over the Paulisa and Romaka Siddhāntas, may be appealed to as not

[1] This opinion of Varāha has been confirmed by modern European scholars. Burgess (from whose translations of the *Sūrya Siddhānta* we have already quoted) remarks, "in regard to . . . the amount of the annual precession of the equinoxes, the relative size of the sun and moon as compared with the earth, the greatest equation of the centre of the sun, the Hindus are more nearly correct than the Greeks." (*Journal of the American Oriental Society*, vol. vi. p. 480.)

[2] *The Pañchasiddhântikâ.* Edited by G. Thibaut, ch. i. § 3.

conveying the impression that when Varāha wrote his co-religionists and scientists were accepting, wholesale and with avidity, Grecian astronomic methods in place of their own already well-established native science. It is true that in Varāha's work many words evidently of Grecian origin are to be met with; and some scholars have claimed that these "Greek terms occurring in Varāhamihira's writings are conclusive proofs of the Greek origin of Hindu astronomy." That such terms should occur in a work professedly a *resumé* of five astronomic treatises—some of them Indian, and some European—can scarcely be considered as conclusive proof that in the writer's time no purely Indian astronomic science existed. Varāha's writings suggest an author interested in comparing the resemblances and the differences to be met with in home and foreign methods, rather than one introducing for the first time important astronomic truths to the notice of his readers.

It may be further urged that the claims to antiquity in Sanscrit astronomical works are so well known, that those who adopt the Grecian theory must necessarily throw discredit in a very wholesale manner on all their authors. Bentley's furious diatribes may be quoted as an extreme example of the way in which the evidence of such Sanscrit claimants to antiquity is sometimes dealt with; and it may be pointed out that such violent denunciation cannot be looked on as convincing argument.

"The fact is," writes Bentley, "that literary forgeries are now so common in India, that we can hardly know what book is genuine, and what not: perhaps there is not one book in a hundred, nay, probably in a thousand, that is not a forgery, in some point of view or other; and even those that are allowed or supposed to be genuine, are found to be full of interpolations, to answer some particular ends: nor need we be surprised at all this, when we consider the facilities they have for forgeries, as well as their own general inclination and interest in following that profession; for to give the appearance of antiquity to their books and authors increases their value, at least in the eyes of some. Their universal propensity to forgeries, ever since the introduction of the modern system of astronomy and immense periods of years, in A.D. 538, are but too well known to require any further elucidation than those already given. They are under no restraint of laws, human or divine, and subject to no punishment, even if detected in the most flagrant literary impositions." [1]

It is unnecessary now to further pursue the pros and cons of what has hitherto been said and written on the vexed questions as to the originality and antiquity of astronomy in India, and especially as to the Indian acquaintance with the twelve-fold divisions of the Zodiac, and the date of the fixation of the initial point in their Zodiac. We have seen that by the majority the Grecian and modern theory is the favoured one.

Within the last quarter of a century, however, an unexpected reinforcement has come into the field, in aid of the disheartened and nearly silenced minority, who still believe in a great antiquity for the science of astronomy in India.

The researches of archæologists in Western Asia have of late brought to our knowledge vast hoards of information concerning the ancient inhabitants of Babylonia and Assyria, and the surrounding highlands and plains; amongst other matters, concerning the science of astronomy possessed by these peoples.

[1] *A Historical View of the Hindu Astronomy*, etc., p. 181.

In 1874, a Paper entitled *The Astronomy and Astrology of the Babylonians* was read by Professor Sayce before the "Society of Biblical Archæology,' and since that date other Papers, by various authors, dealing with the subject have appeared in the same Society's *Proceedings.* Also in the *Zeitschrift für Assyriologie*, articles have been contributed by such writers as Epping and Strassmaier, Oppert, Mayer, Mahler, Jensen, Lehmann, and others, in which the calendars and astronomical methods in use in Mesopotamia are discussed.

Epping and Strassmaier's *Astronomisches aus Babylon* and Jensen's *Die Kosmologie der Babylonier*, are important volumes devoted to these same matters.

Whatever else concerning the subject of all these writings remains uncertain and open to discussion, some facts are clearly established. We now know that the inhabitants of Babylonia in a remote age (certainly as early as the fourth millenium B.C.) were acquainted with the twelve divisions of the Zodiac, and that these divisions were imagined under figures closely resembling in almost every instance those now depicted on our celestial globes. The calendar used by the Accadians, and later by the Semitic Babylonians and Assyrians, was indeed based on the observance of the Zodiacal constellations and of the journeyings through them of the sun and moon. The varying positions of the planets, Mercury, Venus, Mars, Jupiter, and Saturn are also noted by references to the Zodiacal asterisms: and not only Zodiacal, but several of the extra-Zodiacal ancient constellations are represented on the monuments.

All this information gained from the cuneiform tablets concerning the science of astronomy in Western Asia must undoubtedly affect the judgment of enquirers into the history of the same science in India.

Now that it is clearly proved that 3,000 B.C. and earlier the twelve-fold fanciful signs of the Solar Zodiac were known to the inhabitants of Babylonia, it cannot any longer be asserted dogmatically that the inhabitants of India must have waited till 300 B.C. to learn this twelve-fold division from Grecian astronomers after the date of Alexander's conquest.

But again as regards the fixation of the initial

point of the distinctively Indian Lunar Zodiac, or circle of the Nakshatras, at the "end of Revatî, and the beginning of Açvinî," that is to say, at a point not far from the first degree of Aries—cuneiform tablets teach us the important fact that long before the equinoctial point coincided with any of the degrees of Aries, that constellation was the leader of the Zodiacal series—inasmuch as the month Bar zig-gar (Accadian) the "Sacrifice of righteousness," that is, the month when the sun was in conjunction with Aries, always in the tablets appears as the 1st month of the year.[1]

These late revelations of archæology seem to strike at the root of the main arguments relied on by the advocates of the Grecian and modern origin of astronomic science in India; and this being the case, it is possible to turn with unbiassed minds

[1] This fact is admitted (see art. "Zodiac," sub-heading "first sign," *Encyclopædia Britannica*). But it is a fact opposed to the hitherto received opinion touching the necessary connexion of the equinoctial point and of the initial point of the Zodiac. "A prehistoric reform" of the calendar is supposed, and corrections of the ancient texts to suit this reform, are suggested. Until traces of such reform and corrections can be shown to exist, the evidence of the tablets may still be cited as pointing to a year counted from the sun's entry into Aries, in the earliest ages of Babylonian civilization.

to a consideration of the teachings of Sanscrit literature, and endeavour to learn from them what is the real truth as to the acquaintance of ancient Indian authors with the figures of the Zodiac and other astronomic phenomena.

The opinion has been very generally adopted, as has been said, that in the Rig Veda there is no mention of any of the twelve figures of the Solar Zodiac. Some few writers have contended that occasional references to these figures are to be met with, and this question has been argued on etymological grounds. My entire ignorance of the Sanscrit language prevents me from at all following the arguments employed in this discussion. And here it may be said, and said with good reason, that for the discussion of points connected with Vedic literature, writers ignorant of the language in which the Vedas were composed are but ill equipped for the task. At every step I keenly feel my own disqualifications; but many translations and commentaries on the Rig Veda are in existence; and without entering into etymological questions, it has seemed to me that broad astronomic explanations of some of the myths might be supplied, if only the possibility of the Vedic Rishis having been acquainted with the strange figures of the celestial sphere should be admitted. In this paper I am anxious to draw the attention of those who can study Vedic texts in their original language to these possible explanations. Those only who know Sanscrit are really qualified to judge finally whether the suggestions here made can be sustained on further enquiry into the Vedas. If the interpretations of Vedic myths here proposed are correct—no doubt corroboration will be found for them in the Sanscrit names and epithets of mythic personages. If no such corroborations are to be met with, the probabilities in favour of the correctness of the astronomic interpretations will be greatly diminished.

But to return to our subject. It is sometimes argued that the Vedic bards could not have been acquainted with the twelve-fold division of the Zodiac, as otherwise these great constellations would surely have claimed at their hands clear and outspoken notice. With this argument I cannot fully agree. Even before pointing out the important place which I believe astronomical phenomena hold in the Rig Veda, I would draw attention to the fact that according to the generally received and non - astronomic explanation of the myths, it is necessary to suppose that still more striking and important natural phenomena than those connected with the constellations of the Zodiac — phenomena with which the Vedic bards must certainly have been acquainted—were almost entirely ignored by the authors of the Rig Veda. It is true that some great scholars claim on linguistic grounds a solar origin for much Vedic imagery and nomenclature; yet when the hymns are examined in translations, and the notes and commentaries which accompany these translations are studied, the impression left on the mind of any reader unacquainted with Sanscrit must be that very little attention or honour is given to sun, moon, or stars, in comparison to that so freely lavished on the elements of fire, air and water, and on the mysterious properties of the juice of the Soma plant.

The beauty of the dawn is almost the only celestial glory that appears to appeal with any insistence to the imaginations of the Vedic Rishis.

If out of the more than one thousand hymns of the Rig Veda, not one is addressed to the moon, and on the most liberal calculation considerably less than a hundred to the sun, under any aspect, it need not be cause for wonder if the constellations of the Zodiac are not remembered. The poets of the Rig Veda, however ignorant of astronomy, and at whatever age they lived, must have sometimes lifted their eyes above the sacrificial fire and its smoke, above the rain and storm-clouds, above their altars and libations of Soma. They must have often seen "the sun when it shined" and "the moon walking in brightness," and if they so rarely hymned these great luminaries with whose appearance and existence they so certainly were acquainted, it would prove no ignorance on their part of the twelve-fold division of the Zodiac and its quaintly imagined figures, were it indeed the case that all mention of these figures is absent from the Rig Veda.

But as has been stated above, my desire is to draw attention to possible astronomic interpretations of many of the Vedic myths, and the adoption of such interpretations would necessarily entail a reversal of the dictum that all mention of the twelve-fold Zodiac is absent from the Rig Veda.

Those who have studied this wonderful and mysterious collection of hymns most constantly and deeply are obliged to confess that it is still very imperfectly understood, and though it is agreed unanimously that the Gods of the Veda are personifications of the phenomena of nature, yet as to the exact phenomena underlying the various Vedic myths there is among scholars much difference of opinion. It is impossible not to feel in reading the hymns and the many speculations, notes, and comments appended to them, that notwithstanding all the labour and research bestowed on the work, much of this ancient Veda still remains a cypher, for the right understanding of which the modern reader does not possess the key.

Guided by the teachings of archæology, I now make the suggestion that the key to this cypher may perhaps be found in crediting the authors of the Veda with a somewhat advanced knowledge of astronomy, and an acquaintance with the, to us, apparently fanciful constellations of the celestial sphere and Zodiac; and in assuming that the figures of the "ancient constellations" often supplied the basis of Vedic imagery.

To pursue this possible clue towards the understanding of the myths, it were much to be desired that all students should be acquainted with the names and positions in the heavens of the forty-five constellations—so well distinguished by the epithet "ancient"—and that they should master some of the more easily observed conditions of their diurnal and annual apparent movements, as also those of the sun and moon, and further that they should have learnt what changes in the scenery of the heavens have been brought about by the slow movement known to astronomers as the "precession of the equinoxes."

Classical and philological scholars have however so rarely time and attention to spare from their own intensely interesting and important studies that as a rule astronomical phenomena are not much observed or considered by them. The accompanying diagrams drawn from a celestial precessional globe may, it is hoped, enable those, who have not as yet devoted thought to such subjects, to judge for themselves of the reasonableness or otherwise of the following astronomic suggestions concerning the most important of the Vedic gods.

According to A. A. Macdonell — who in his late work *Vedic Mythology* has summed up clearly and compendiously the opinions of a host of scholars on the nature of the Vedic gods— Indra is the favourite national god of the Rig Veda; he is celebrated in 250 hymns, a greater number than that "devoted to any other god, and very nearly one-fourth of the total number of hymns in the Rig Veda."[1]

What may be called the central myths related of Indra, stripped of all epithet and ornament, relate that, invigorated by copious draughts of Soma, Indra fights with, overcomes, and drives from heaven and earth a demon called Vritra or Ahi, who is represented under the form of a dragon, serpent or water snake. Indra also searches for, finds, and releases cows which had

[1] Macdonell, *Vedic Mythology*, p. 54.

been stolen from the gods (or according to some commentators, from the angirasas, or priests). Indra bestows on his worshippers all the blessings of plenty, especially he is the dispenser of rain.

According to the usual non-astronomic explanations of these myths, Indra, an "atmospheric god,"[1] is "primarily the thunder god" who conquers "the demons of drought or darkness," or again, "Indra[2] is a personification of the phenomena of the firmament, particularly in the capacity of sending down rain. This property is metaphorically described as a conflict with the clouds which are reluctant to part with their watery stores until assailed and penetrated by the thunder-bolt of Indra; . . . the cloud is personified as a demon named Ahi or Vritra . . . a popular myth represents him (Indra) also as the discoverer and rescuer of the cows, either of the priests or of the gods which had been stolen by an *Asura* named Pañi or Vala."

Macdonell, alluding to the same incident, ob-

[1] Macdonell, *Vedic Mythology*, p. 66.

[2] Wilson, *Rig Veda*, Introduction, pp. xxx.-xxxi.

serves:[1] These "cows released by Indra may, in many cases, refer to the waters, for we have seen that the latter are occasionally compared with lowing cows. Thus Indra is said to have found the cows for man when he slew the dragon. . . . But the cows may also in other cases be conceived as connected with Indra's winning of light, for the ruddy beams of dawn issuing from the blackness of night are compared with cattle coming out of their dark stalls. Again, though clouds play no great part in the Rig Veda under their literal name (*abhra*, etc.), it can hardly be denied that, as containing the waters, they figure mythologically to a considerable extent under the name of cow (*go*), as well as udder (*ūdhar*) . . . thus the rain-clouds are probably meant when it is said that the cows roared at the birth of Indra."

At the close of the section devoted to Indra, Macdonell refers to the probably pre-Vedic origin of the Indra myths. He says:[2] "The name of Indra occurs only twice in the Avesta. Beyond the fact of his being no god, but only a demon,

[1] *Vedic Mythology*, p. 59.

[2] *Ibid.*, pp. 66.

his character there is uncertain. Indra's distinctive Vedic epithet *vrtrahan* [Vritra-slayer] also occurs in the Avesta in the form of *verethraghna*, which is, however, unconnected with Indra or the thunderstorm myth, designating merely the God of Victory. Thus it is probable that the Indo-Iranian period possessed a god approaching to the Vedic form of the Vrtra-slaying Indra. It is even possible that beside the thundering god of heaven, the Indo-European period may have known as a distinct conception a thunder-god, gigantic in size, a mighty eater and drinker, who slays the dragon with his lightning bolt."

In reading the Indra hymns in the Veda, and in trying to fit them to the explanation given in the passages quoted, a constant and very disagreeable strain is put on the imagination; it must, for instance, attempt to grasp and hold, at the same time, two very far apart opinions as to the nature of the demon Vritra. Vritra is to be thought of as a demon of darkness, and as a demon of drought; the cows are clouds, they are also ruddy beams of light!

Darkness and drought are not to be easily

bracketed together. Drought is in all lands, India not excepted, connected with a long continuance of bright and stainless skies. The appearance then of a little cloud "like a man's hand" is the joyously hailed precursor of "the sound of abundance of rain."

Again, the driving away of a snake-like cloud is no forcible simile by which to describe in myth the advent of rain in India—rain which to be of any use is no mere refreshing shower, but a long-continued downpour from clouds not hastily dispersed.

Indra's action first in driving away the cloud-demon Vritra, and then in seeking for the beneficial cloud cows, is also contradictory.

For the reconciling of many of these contradictions the astronomic interpretation of the Indra-Vritra myths is as follows:—Indra may still retain all his atmospheric attributes of sending down rain but—*Indra is primarily and essentially a personification of the summer solstice.*

The summer solstice in India is an all-important agricultural epoch; it brings with it "the rainy season," the real spring of the Indian year. Before this season all the land is parched and arid, and vegetation is at a standstill.

The punctuality of the rains in many parts of India is so exact that the farmer foretells their arrival not only to the day, but to the hour. In good years heavy and almost incessant rain lasts for two or even three months. Indra, as a personification of the season which so punctually brings the rain, is an atmospheric god, the enemy of the demon of drought. But Indra is more than this: many praises are bestowed on Indra in the Rig Veda for deeds which cannot easily be explained on the simple atmospheric theory. "Indra is the highest of all" is the refrain of many Vedic verses; "Indra placed the sun high in the sky," "Indra tore off one wheel of the sun's chariot," "Indra stopped the tawny coursers of the sun." Now all these phrases are at once and clearly to be interpreted if we think of Indra as the personification of the summer solstice, and especially of the solstice in India, where at that season of the year the sun attains to the very zenith, and thus Indra associated with the *sun* under one figure of speech is spoken of as "highest of all," and in a slightly varied figure associated with the *season*, is said to have "*placed* the sun high in the sky." Or again translating into myth the very meaning of the word solstice or "*the sun being made to stand*," we read that Indra "tore off the wheel of the chariot of the sun," and "stopped his tawny coursers." Indra is, I cannot but believe, not merely an atmospheric god; he is the god of the summer solstice. And if this should be the case, what then may Vritra be? Is the demon of the solstitial Indra personified as only a snake-like cloud? It is impossible to think so. The astronomic interpretation of the myth I would propose is that — *a snake-like constellation*, not a snake-like cloud, is the representation of the demon Vritra.

On the celestial sphere many serpents and dragons are represented, but the far-reaching constellation Hydra exceeds all the others in its enormous length from head to tail. No very brilliant stars mark the asterism, nor in the grouping of its stars is there anything especially snake-like. For some reason other than its appeal to the eye did astronomers of old invest with all the horrors of the Hydra-form the monotonous length of this space on the vault of the skies.

This reason may be arrived at, with almost certainty, in studying, with the help of a precessional globe, the position in the heavens of this constellation in different ages of the world's history. So studying, we shall find that 4,000 B.C. — or to be more precise, one or two hundred years earlier—Hydra extended its enormous length for more than 90° symmetrically along one astronomically important (though invisible) mathematical line — the line of the heavenly equator — and was at the same date accurately bisected by another equally important mathematical line, namely the colure of the summer solstice (see Plate IX.).

Almost irresistibly, as it appears to me, the conviction forces itself on the mind, in considering the position held by the constellation Hydra 4,000 B.C., that it was at that date that this baleful figure was first traced in imagination on the sky, there fitly to represent the power of physical (and may we not suppose also, of moral?) darkness—a great and terrible power—but a power ever and

PLATE IX.

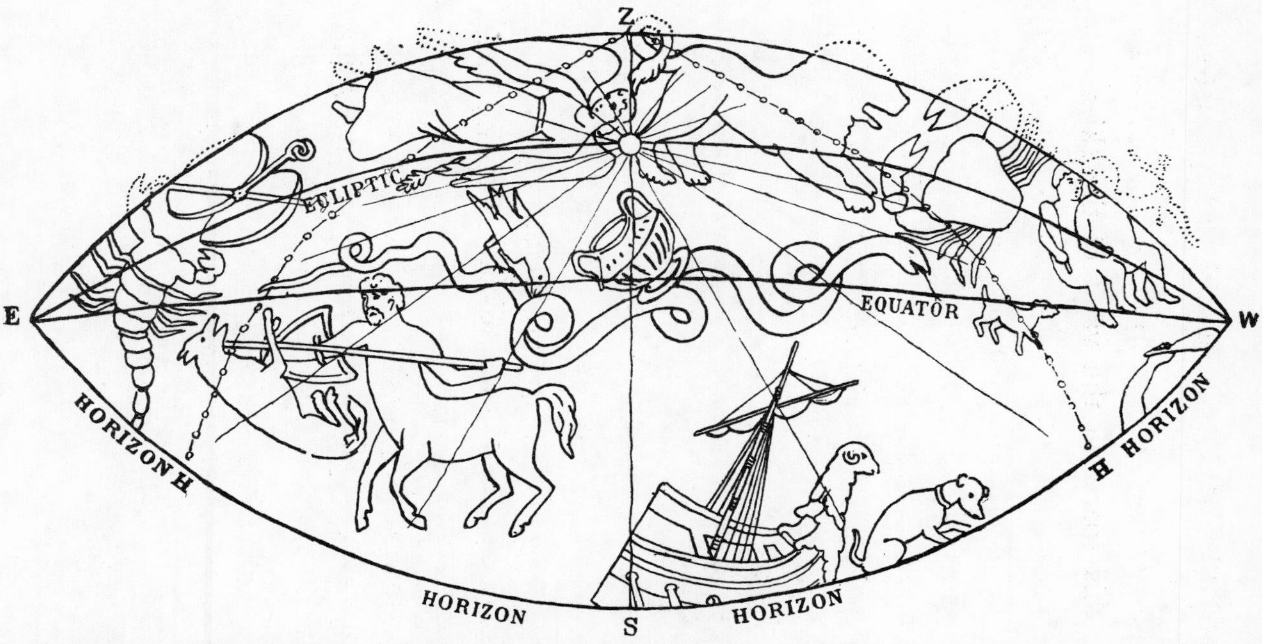

Position of the Sun amongst the Constellations at Summer Solstice, 4,000 B.C. Observer in Lat. 40° N. Constellations between the lines H Z and Z H invisible all through the night of Summer Solstice.

[*To face p.* 118.

ever again to be conquered by the victorious power of light. In astronomic myth this power was represented as that of the sun at the season of its highest culmination, the season of the summer solstice. For an observer in the temperate northern zone all through the long nights of mid-winter, the whole length of the dreadful Hydra was at the date named visible above the horizon. The dark midwinter season was therefore the time of the Hydra's greatest glory. At every season of the year, except at that of midsummer, some portion of the monster's form was visible during some part of the night. But at the summer solstice no star in the constellation might show itself for ever so short a time.[1]

The supposed latitude of the observer in Plate IX. is 40° N., a latitude considerably to the north of any part of India; but it is to be remembered that the Indra-Vritra myth cannot be claimed with any certainty as a purely and originally Indian myth, for, as Macdonell points out (as quoted above), there

[1] Plate IX. represents the constellations above the horizon, *but invisible at noon at the midsummer solstice.* It therefore represents those above the horizon, *and visible at midwinter midnight.*

is a probability that "the Indo-Iranian period possessed a god approaching to the Vedic form of the Vrtra-slaying Indra," and that "it is even possible that beside the thundering god of heaven, the Indo - European period may have known as a distinct conception a thunder-god, gigantic in size, a mighty eater and drinker, who slays the dragon with his lightning bolt."[1]

For the *origin* of this world-wide myth, therefore, we should not look to the tropical Indian Zone; but it is in Indian latitudes that we should look for an explanation of the physical phenomena *hymned by Vedic bards in the distinctly Indian development of the Indra-Vritra myth.* I believe that in thus tracing the course of the Indra story from temperate to tropical latitudes, we shall find a reason for the contradictory attributes assigned to the demon Vritra, namely those of darkness and drought.

In northern latitudes winter is distinctly the *dark* season; in tropical India there is little or no perceptible difference between the darkness of winter and summer. But in India winter is dis-

[1] V. p. 114.

PLATE X.

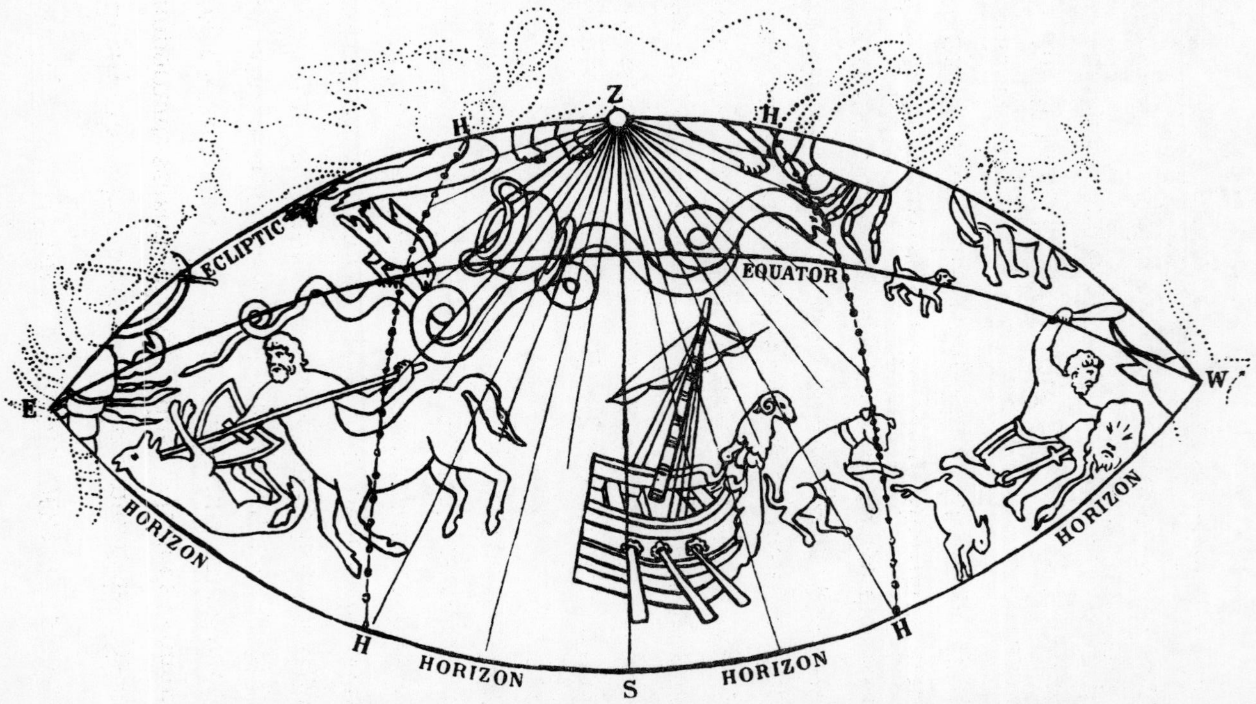

Portion of Sun at Summer Solstice, 3,000 B.C. Observer in Lat. 23° N.
Constellations between the lines H H Z and Z H H invisible all through the night of Summer Solstice.

[*To face p.* 121.

tinctly the dry season. Midsummer is the all-important season of the rains. Indra's conquest over Vritra, or the arrival of solstitial rains, marked by the disappearance of the constellation Hydra from the sky, was mythologically in the Vedas described as Indra's conquest over the demon of *drought*, but still traditionally—for the power of tradition is great—even in India Indra retained the attributes of the conqueror over the demon of *darkness*.

At Plate X. a drawing is given of the southern heavens and of the constellations—invisible at midsummer and visible at midwinter, above the horizon of an observer in latitude 23° N. at the date 3000 B.C., a thousand years later than the date referred to in Plate IX. For reasons which will appear more clearly when we come to the discussion of the Soma myth, it is to about this date that I would attribute the composition of many of the Vedic hymns.

But if Indra is to be considered as representing the summer solstice, and Vritra as representing the constellation Hydra, we must surely expect some astronomic interpretation for Soma—Soma by which the mighty Indra is invigorated and enabled to triumph gloriously over the demon. According to non-astronomic explanations, "the concrete terrestrial plant and the intoxicating juice extracted therefrom" are considered to be the basis of the mythology of Soma. It is admitted that in post-Vedic literature Soma is a regular name of the moon, which is regarded as being drunk up by the gods, and so waning. Some writers point to the possibility that even in the Rig Veda, "in the Soma hymns there may occasionally lurk a veiled identification of ambrosia and the moon, . . . but on the whole, with the few exceptions generally admitted, it appears to be certain that to the seers of the Rig Veda the god Soma is a personification of the terrestrial plant and juice."[1]

One German writer, Hillebrandt, very strongly upholds the view that Soma in the Rig Veda "often personifies the moon,"[2] and especially according to him is this the case in the 114 hymns of Maṇḍala IX., all addressed to Soma

[1] Macdonell, *Vedic Mythology*, p. 113.
[2] *Ibid.*

pavamāna, or "purified Soma," prepared for and quaffed by Indra to invigorate him for the Vritra combat.

That Soma in the Rig Veda is primarily the moon, and that the moon is symbolized and always more or less directly referred to in the Vedic hymns to Soma, fits in, as must be evident to the readers of this paper, with the astronomic theories advocated in it. If we consider that Indra's conquest over Vritra represents the god of the summer solstice, with his bright weapons, conquering, and driving from heaven and earth the constellation Hydra, we can easily understand how in this contest Indra might be strengthened by copious draughts of Soma, *i.e.* by the bright light of the full moon flooding the heavens with radiance and enfeebling all but the brightest stars.

But a further confirmation of the lunar character of Soma, and an elucidation of the imagery of the Soma pavamāna hymns of Maṇḍala IX., are to be found if—still crediting the Vedic Rishis with a knowledge of the ancient constellations—we study the position of these constellations at the date

3,000 B.C. (see Plate XI.)[1] At that date the full moon of the midsummer or solstitial season was always to be observed in the constellation Aquarius. With this thought in our mind as we read the mystical hymns of Maṇḍala IX., in which Soma is so often described as rushing impetuously to the vase or pitcher, and as surrounded by celestial waters, with many other such expressions, we easily recognise an allusion to the *midsummer full moon in the constellation Aquarius;* and when further we read the legend so often repeated, that the eagle brought the Soma to Indra, or to the sacrifice, we have only to look at the celestial globe to see the eagle (Aquila) directing its flight towards the pitcher of Aquarius—and to remember that the very night before the moon attained the celestial vase, it would have been on the same meridian as the constellation Aquila; and the imaginative Vedic bard might then describe it as borne along by the eagle, — one of the most glorious constellations in that part of the sky.

[1] Lunar dates are variable. The full moon *nearest* to the summer solstice might have been observed somewhat to the east or the west of its position in the diagram, but always in the constellation Aquarius.

PLATE XI.

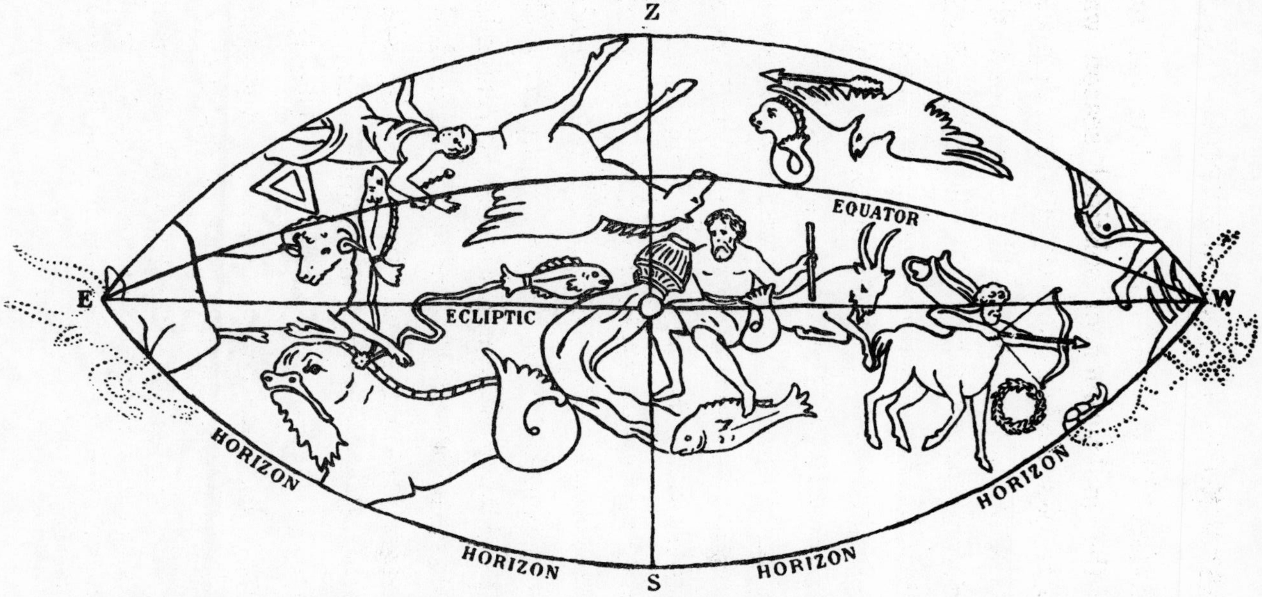

Position of Moon amongst the Constellations at Summer Solstice, and of the Sun at Winter Solstice, 3,000 B.C. Observer in Lat. 23° N.

[*To face p.* 124.

In one hymn especially devoted to the legend of the Soma-bearing eagle (or hawk), allusion to the small but well-marked-out constellation Sagitta (the arrow) may be detected. In Wilson's translation of Maṇḍala IV. 27 (vol. iii. p. 174), we read: "When the hawk screamed (with exultation) on his descent from heaven, and (the guardians of the *Soma*) perceived that the *Soma* was (carried away) by it, then, the archer Kriṣánu, pursuing with the speed of thought, and stringing his bow, let fly an arrow against it."

Now to turn to another important Vedic deity, Agni.

Agni is classed, according to Macdonell, amongst terrestrial gods, but he points out that in some passages he is to be identified with the sun. Wilson describes Agni as comprising[1] "the element of *Fire* under three aspects: 1st, as it exists on earth, not only as culinary or religious fire, but as the heat of digestion and of life, and the vivifying principle of vegetation; 2nd, as it exists in the atmosphere, or mid-heaven, in the form of lightning; and 3rd, as it is manifested in the

[1] Wilson, *Rig Veda*, Introduction, vol. i. pp. xxvii.-xxviii.

heavens, as light, the sun, the dawn, and planetary bodies." And—having enumerated various deities who in the hymns appear as manifestations of the sun—he adds, "still, however, the sun does not hold that prominent place in the *Vaidik* liturgy which he seems to have done in that of the ancient Persians, and he is chiefly venerated as the celestial representative of Fire."

The classification of Agni as a terrestrial god, given by Macdonell, and the order of his "aspects," as given by Wilson, are not in accordance with the theory here advocated, nor, according to Macdonell, is it the classification or order always adhered to by Vedic authorities.

For some very puzzling myths concerning Agni, I believe an astronomic interpretation may be given, and thereby the position of Agni in the *first* place, rather than in the *last*, as a celestial god, may be established.

The Vedic deity Apām Napāt—the son of Waters, is classed by Macdonell as an atmospheric god, and he says,[1] "In the last stanza of the Apām napāt hymn, the deity is invoked as Agni, and must be identified with him," and again,[2] "Agni's

[1] *Vedic Mythology*, p. 70. [2] *Ibid.*, p. 92.

origin in the aerial waters is often referred to. The 'son of waters' has, as has been shown, become a distinct deity." Then turning to other legends regarding Agni he says, "In such passages the lightning form of Agni must be meant. Some of the later hymns of the Rig Veda tell a legend of Agni hiding in the waters and plants, and being found by the gods. . . . In one passage of the Rig Veda also it is stated that Agni rests in all streams; and in the later ritual texts, Agni in the waters is invoked in connexion with ponds and water-vessels. Thus, even in the oldest Vedic period, the waters in which Agni is latent, though not those from which he is produced, may in various passages have been regarded as terrestrial. . . . In any case the notion of Agni in the waters is prominent throughout the Vedas."

To explain this legend, Wilson makes other suggestions. He writes:[1] "The legend of his (Agni's) hiding in the waters, through fear of the enemies of the gods, although alluded to in more than one place, is not very explicitly related . . . . the allusions of the *Súktas* (hymns) may be a figurative intimation of the latent heat existing in water, or a misapprehension of a natural phenomenon which seems to have made a great impression in later times—the

[1] Wilson, *Rig Veda*, Introduction, vol. i. p. xxx.

emission of flame from the surface of water either in the shape of inflammable air, or as the result of submarine volcanic action."

It cannot but be admitted that these myths are puzzling, and that to account for the notion so prominent throughout the Vedas of "Agni in the waters," the various suggestions of "lightning," "latent heat existing in water," "the emission of flame from the surface of the waters, either in the shape of inflammable air or as the result of submarine volcanic action," are inadequate to explain the fact that Agni, whose very name "is the regular designation of fire"[1] should in the hymns be so closely associated with water. Nor are the difficulties concerning "Agni in the waters" to be overcome by the tempting and poetic suggestion, put forward by some writers, that in these passages reference is made to the sun rising in the morning out of the ocean, and again hiding itself beneath the waves at sunset. The composition of the Rig Veda is attributed to Aryan settlers "scattered over the Punjaub and regions lying to the west of the Indus": by such settlers the

[1] Macdonell, *Vedic Mythology*, p. 88.

sun could never have been seen *rising* out of the ocean, for no ocean bounded their horizon on the east. Even the phenomenon of the sun hiding itself at evening in the water, could only have been observed by those who lived on the western *coast*, and it is therefore not easy to imagine why sunrise and sunset should in India have been so closely and constantly associated with a sea horizon.

But if once the acquaintance of the originators of the Agni myths with the Zodiacal figures is admitted, the astronomic interpretation of those relating to Agni in the waters is not difficult; it is as follows:

Agni is the personification of fire, but his chief personification is as the fire of the sun. "*Agni in the waters" is especially the fire of the sun in the celestial waters of Aquarius.* 3,000 B.C. the sun was in conjunction with Aquarius at the time of the *winter solstice.*[1] Those hymns therefore which dwell upon the myths of Agni hiding himself in, being born in, and rising out of the waters,

[1] The position of the sun at the *winter solstice* 3,000 B.C. was identical with that represented at Plate XI. as the position of the full moon at the *summer solstice.*

may be considered as hymns referring to *the sun at the winter solstice in conjunction with the constellation Aquarius*, and therefore as hymns especially suitable for use on the occasion of a great yearly festival held at that season of the year.

European writers often describe the mid-winter sun as *hiding* itself, or as every day withdrawing itself more and more from view. In poetic similes, the snows of winter often crown the head of the aged out-going year, while the in-coming year is represented as a *babe* or *infant*. The appropriateness of such similes is due to the fact, that our calendrical new year is fixed within a few days of the winter solstice. Again, in sober prose, the sun at the time of the winter solstice is said, having attained its lowest point, *to rise* or *begin its upward course* on the ecliptic. It is therefore not difficult to understand how the Vedic Rishis, who appear to have combined the characteristics of poets and of scientific observers of the heavens, should have 3,000 B.C. described *the fire of the solstitial sun, as hiding in, being born in, and rising out of the celestial waters of the constellation Aquarius.*

In this Agni myth, as in that of Indra, we may perceive traces of a pre-Vedic origin. The latitudes in which the Rig Veda was composed are not those in which attention is forcibly drawn to the diminution of the strength and visibility of the sun at the winter season. In the Rig Veda, however, Indra's conquest over darkness as well as over drought is celebrated, and the same *traditional* cause may be assigned for the description of Agni hiding himself at the time of the winter solstice in the waters of Aquarius.

Indra, Soma, and Agni no longer hold the important place in the Hindu Pantheon which they appear to have held in Vedic times, and on the astronomic theory, this fact may partly be accounted for by noticing how slow but inevitable changes in the scenery of the heavens, produced by the precession of the equinoxes, gradually obscured more and more completely the meaning of the *imagery* employed in the hymns to these deities. Indra, if he represents the summer solstice, is indeed still as powerful as ever, and still triumphs over the demon of drought, but no longer is that demon well represented by the snake-like constellation Hydra; for on the night of the summer solstice, after the sun has set, the whole of Hydra is still above the horizon. No longer does the mid-summer full moon bathe its brightness in the celestial waters of Aquarius, nor does the mid-winter sun hide itself in them. The hymns remain, the phenomena they referred to, exist no longer.

But leaving now the subject of the "ancient constellations" and of reference to them in the Rig Veda, let us turn to the second section of the argument in favour of the modern origin of Hindu astronomy as stated above.[1] It is a claim made for the very modern date of 570 A.D. as that for the fixation of the initial point of the Indian Zodiac at the "end of Revatî and the beginning of Açvinî."—This claim I desire to oppose.

It has been admitted by scholars, but almost with a sort of reluctance, that mention is made of some of the Nakshatras in a few of the Rig Veda hymns. The matter is rather avoided than cordially enquired into. It is, however, a question

[1] V. p. 92.

of great and important interest to ascertain, if possible, whether the circle of the Nakshatras was known to the Vedic Rishis, and if it were known, whether the initial point was fixed there, where as we have read, *all schools of Hindu astronomy agree in declaring that the planetary motions commenced at the creation.*[1]

We have learnt from Babylonian archæology that we are no longer forced to assume that only at the date of about 570 A.D. could this initial point have been fixed by Indian astronomers. It therefore need no longer be looked upon as an unreasonable quest to search in the ancient pages of the Rig Veda for indications that this important astronomical point had been fixed, even before Vedic times, as the starting-point of a calendrical and sidereal year—and if we should find such indications in the Rig Veda, they may well out-weigh arguments against the antiquity of this fixation, based upon passages in later works, such as the Yajur and Atharva Vedas.

From the Yajur Veda itself, arguments may be drawn in favour of a year beginning in the

[1] V. p. 93.

month Chaitra,[1] at or before the date of the composition or compilation of that Veda.

In the Taittirîya Sanhitâ (contained in the Yajur Veda) a passage occurs[2] which is translated and commented upon by B. G. Tilak (*The Orion, or Antiquity of the Vedas*, p. 46 *et seq.*). In this passage is discussed the superior suitability of three different days on which worshippers might consecrate themselves for the yearly sacrifice. Not any one of these three days has any connexion with the *spring equinox* or the sun's conjunction with Krittikā. The choice of date for the yearly sacrifice appears to lie between, first, the "Ekâṣhṭakā (day)" of some month not named,[3] but one in the "distressed," or "reversed" period of the year, *i.e.* the mid-winter season; second, the full moon of Phalgunī; and third, the Chaitra full moon. B. G. Tilak, after some pages of comment on the passage referred to, states in his summing

[1] Chaitra is the month which begins, as closely as a luni-solar month may, at the sun's arrival at the initial point of the Hindu Zodiac—the beginning of Aswinī.

[2] Taittirîya Sanhitâ, vii. 4. 8.

[3] At p. 48 he quotes authorities in favour of the Ekâṣhṭakā (day) in this passage meaning the 8th day of the dark half of Mâgha.

up, amongst others, the following conclusions which he has arrived at.

"1st, that in the days of the Taittirîya Sanhitâ the winter solstice occurred before the eighth day of the dark half of Mâgha . . . and that throughout the whole passage the intention of sacrificing at the beginning (real, constructive, or traditional) of the year is quite clear: . . . . 2nd, that the year then commenced with the winter solstice": "3rd, that as there can not be three real beginnings of the year, at an interval of one month each, the passage must be understood as recording a tradition about the Chitrâ full moon and the Phalgunī full moon being once considered as the first days of the year."

This is B. G. Tilak's conclusion; merely judging from the *translation*, the passage might, as it seems to me, be understood as unreservedly recommending the full-moon of Chaitra as the most suitable for the beginning of the sacrifice, for in the text of the Taittirîya Sanhitâ it is said of it, "It has no fault whatsoever."

But in whichever sense the words are understood, this passage from the Yajur Veda may be set against the hymns and lists in the Yajur and

Atharva Vedas, above alluded to,[1] in which Krittikā is celebrated in the first, and Aswinī in the twenty-seventh place.

The fact that the evidence as to the beginning of the year "in the days of the Taittirîya Sanhitâ," is, as it seems, so uncertain, and so contradictory to the opinion based on the hymn in the Taittirîya Brāhmana concerning Krittikā being the leader of the Nakshatras, seems to add interest to the question whether there are, or are not, indications in the Rig Veda that the Indian year was counted from the same point on the ecliptic as at present?[2]

And at once, as it seems to me, on turning to the Rig Veda, on page after page, such indications are to be met with.

The first Nakshatra in the Indian series is named Aswinī (Aswins). The two chief stars in that Nakshatra are the twin stars, as they may fairly be

[1] V. p. 94.

[2] At present the month Chaitra in most parts of India is the first month of the Hindu year. The beginning of the year is measured by the return of the sun to the same point in the Zodiac: at present the beginning of the Lunar Mansion Aswinī. (See *Indian Calendar*, p. 45.)

called, α and β Arietis—stars of almost equal radiance. The joyous hymns addressed to the twin heroes, the Aswins, I would claim as new-year hymns composed in honour of these *stars*, whose appearance before sunrise heralded the approach of the great festival-day of the Hindu new year.

The Hindu year is a sidereal year. It is counted at present in most parts of India from a fixed point on the ecliptic, not from a season. It is a calendrical not a cosmic year. Only one apparently small change in the method of counting the years would now require to be made, and again the Aswins might be hymned by the Hindus as the "wondrous," and "not untruthful," *stars*, marking by their heliacal rising a new year's festival—a festival to be held on the 15th, or full moon's day.

The Hindu year is now counted from the new moon immediately *preceding* the sun's arrival at the initial point of the lunar Zodiac. The first of Chaitra (the first of the light half of Chaitra) never falls later than the 12th of April, and may arrive a month earlier. If the year were to be counted from the same initial point, but from the first new moon *following* instead of that *preceding* the sun's arrival at that point, there would be the difference of a whole month in the range of the month Chaitra. The first day of its bright half would then never arrive before the 12th of April, and might fall a month later.

For the interpretation of the Vedic hymns to the Aswins I would make the provisional suggestion, that when these hymns were composed, the year was so counted from the new moon *following* and not from that *preceding* the arrival of the sun at "the end of Revatî and the beginning of Açvinî." In support of this provisional theory, let us first read the summing up of the Aswinī myths, and of the difficulties and uncertainties surrounding them, according to the present modes of explanation; and then let us consider the astronomic method of interpretation above proposed.

We read that[1] "Next to Indra, Agni, and Soma, the twin deities named the Aśvins are the most prominent in the Rig Veda, judged by the frequency with which they are invoked. They are celebrated

[1] Macdonell, *Vedic Mythology*, p. 49.

in more than fifty entire hymns and in parts of several others, while their name occurs more than 400 times. Though they hold a distinct position among the deities of light and their appellation is Indian, their connexion with any definite phenomenon of light is so obscure, that their original nature has been a puzzle to Vedic interpreters from the earliest times. This obscurity makes it probable that the origin of these gods is to be sought in a pre-Vedic period. . . . . The Aśvins are young, the T. S. (Taittirīya Sanhitâ) even describing them as the youngest of the gods. They are at the same time ancient. They are bright, lords of lustre, of golden brilliancy, and honey-hued. . . . . They possess profound wisdom and occult power. The two most distinctive and frequent epithets of the Aśvins are *dasra*, 'wondrous,' which is almost entirely limited to them, and *nāsatya*, which is generally explained to mean 'not untrue. . . .' Their car . . . . moves round heaven. It traverses heaven and earth in a single day as the car of the sun and that of Uṣas (the Dawn) are also said to do. . . . The time of their appearance is often said to be the early dawn, when 'darkness still stands among the ruddy cows' and they yoke their car to descend to earth and receive the offerings of worshippers. Uṣas (the Dawn) awakes them. They follow after Uṣas in their car. At the yoking of their car Uṣas is born. Thus their relative time seems to have been between dawn and sunrise. But Savitṛ (the sun) is once said to set their car in motion before the dawn. Occasionally the appearance of the Aśvins, the kindling of the sacrificial fire, the break of dawn, and sunrise seem to be spoken of as simultaneous. The Aśvins are invoked to come to the offering not only at their natural time, but also in the evening or at morning, noon, and sunset. . . . In the A. B. (Aitareya Brahmana) the Aśvins as well as Uṣas and Agni are stated to be gods of dawn; and in the Vedic ritual they are connected with sunrise. . . . . The Aśvins may originally have been conceived as finding and restoring or rescuing the vanished light of the sun. In the Rig Veda they have come to be typically succouring divinities." . . . Again, at p. 51, the writer adds, "Quite a number of legends illustrating the succouring power of the Aśvins are referred to in the Rig Veda." Here follows an enumeration of many miraculous "protections," and cures,—and then[1] "The opinion of Bergaigne and others that the various miracles attributed to the Aśvins are anthropomorphized forms of solar phenomena (the

[1] Macdonell, *Vedic Mythology*, p. 53.

healing of the blind man thus meaning the release of the sun from darkness), seems to lack probability. At the same time the legend of Atri may be a reminiscence of a myth explaining the restoration of the vanished sun. As to the physical basis of the Aśvins, the language of the Ṛṣis is so vague that they themselves do not seem to have understood what phenomenon these deities represented . . . . what they actually represented puzzled even the oldest commentators mentioned by Yāska. That scholar remarks that some regarded them (the Aśvins) as Heaven and Earth (as does the S. B.—Satapatha Brahmana), others as Day and Night, others as sun and moon, while the 'legendary writers' took them to be 'two kings, performers of holy acts.' Yāska's own opinion is obscure."

In contrast to all these vague and often contradictory explanations, the astronomical suggestion made at page 137 may to some appear too matter-of-fact and prosaic. But that a firm and scientific base should underlie mythical and imaginative similes does not in reality detract from their poetic excellence. Indeed, an added fitness, and therefore an added beauty, is to be recognized in the Aswin hymns, when we can think of them as addressed to well-known and beneficent deities presiding over the new year—deities who manifested themselves in the earliest dawn of the new year's morning under the form of two beautiful and easily to be recognised *stars*, and to whom their worshippers appealed for "protection," through the unknown dangers of the future year.

I give two diagrams to illustrate the fact that the time of the rising of the stars α and β Arietis must necessarily, on such a new year's festival as above proposed, have taken place in some years before the first intimation of dawn, in others a few minutes before the time of sunrise.

It is of course to be borne in mind that the Vedic years were luni-solar. The actual point therefore on the ecliptic at which the conjunction of sun and moon—or new moon—took place, and from which each year was counted, varied in different years to the extent of nearly 30 degrees. The diagram, Plate XII. Figs. 1 and 2, represents the maximum and minimum distance between the rising of the Yoga stars of the Nakshatra Aswinī, and of the sun on the 15th or full-moon's day of the first month of a luni-solar year; counted from the first

PLATE XII.

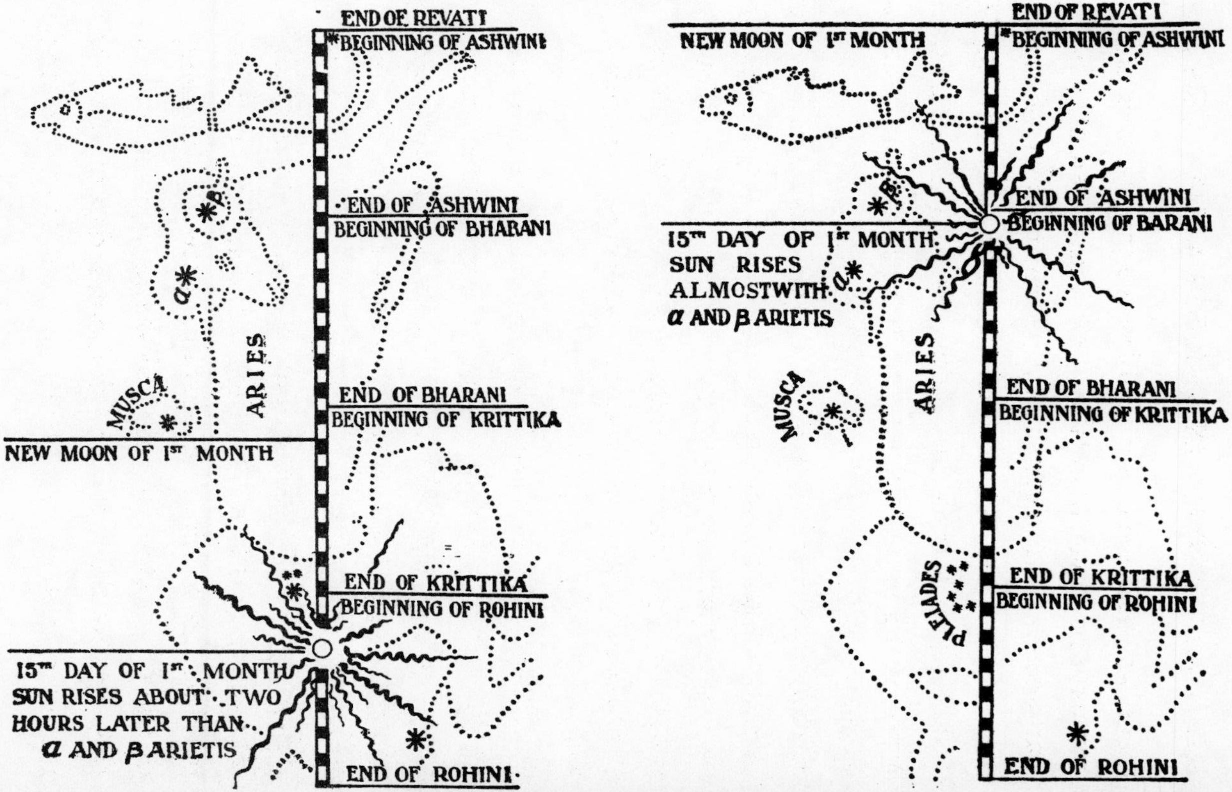

The Vedic Aswins and the Indian Calendar.

[To face p. 142.

conjunction of sun and moon *following* the sun's arrival at the "end of Revatî and the beginning of Açvinî."

It will be seen from the diagram that something more than two hours was the longest interval that, according to the presumed method of counting the Vedic year, elapsed between the appearance of α and β Arietis and of the sun above the horizon.

This astronomic interpretation accounts for the varying times noted in the hymns for the appearance of the Aswins. It also accounts, as it seems to me, for the general tone of the hymns, but as regards the long series of miraculous "protections" of the Aswins, accorded by them to many sick, aged, and decrepit personages, it does not at first sight account.

We have seen that Bergaigne and others have opined that the various miracles attributed to the Aswins are "anthropomorphized forms of solar phenomena," and with this view the astronomic interpretation, when fully followed out to its logical end, agrees.

But at first sight we wonder how the sun at the beginning of the calendrical year could, *in*

Vedic times, be described as in any way especially sick, aged, or decrepit.

3,000 B.C., when, as we have seen, the winter solstice was in Aquarius, the Indian calendrical and sidereal year, such as has been supposed, would have begun at its earliest a month and a half *after* the solstice.[1] The sun *at* the winter solstice, may be, and often is, described as pale, weak, sick and old; but at the beginning of a calendrical year, a month and a half *after* the solstice, the sun no longer could have been thought of as requiring the miraculous protection of the heralding Aswins.

To help in solving this difficulty, recourse may again wisely be had to Babylonian astronomic lore. The fanciful legends regarding the Aswins, considered only by themselves, can scarcely yield a sufficiently firm foundation on which to build the far-reaching theory I now desire to bring forward

[1] If the Hindu year were *now* counted from the new moon *following* instead of that *preceding* the sun's arrival at the initial point of the Zodiac, owing to the precession of the equinoxes, the year would begin at earliest twenty-one days after the *spring equinox*. Since 3,000 B.C. the seasons have advanced by more than two months, as regards their position amongst the stars.

concerning them; a theory on all fours with one I ventured some years ago to propound in reference to Babylonian astronomy, in a Paper entitled the "Accadian Calendar."[1] It was there suggested that the probable date for the origin of that Calendar was about 6,000 B.C. The fact was pointed out that Aries, in the most ancient Accadian and Babylonian astronomical works, always appears as leader of the signs and of the year, and stress was laid on the unlikelihood that this constellation should have been chosen for this leading post at a date when the sun's entry into it did not correspond with any one of the four well-marked natural divisions of the year, *i.e.* the solstices or equinoxes. But as on the cuneiform tablets Aries appears as *leader* long before the time when the sun sojourned in that constellation during the first month following *the equinox*, it was suggested that it was when the *solstitial not the equinoctial* point coincided with the first degree of Aries, that the Accadian calendrical scheme had first been drawn up; namely about 6,000 B.C.

A corroboration of the view then put for-

[1] *Proceedings of Society of Biblical Archæology*, January 1892.

ward is to be drawn from a further study of the Accadian month names. The first three month names, in Accadian, referred, as scholars have pointed out, to the first three constellations of the Zodiac.

(1.) The month of the "sacrifice of righteousness" to Aries.

(2.) The month of the "propitious Bull" to Taurus.

(3.) The month of "the Twins" to Gemini.

The twelfth and thirteenth names in the same series seem to refer equally clearly to a year originally counted as beginning at the *winter solstice*. They are called respectively:

"12th. The month of sowing of seed."—"13th. The dark month of sowing."

For the sowing of most cereals, late autumn and early winter are the favoured seasons. Many crops however are sown in early spring. There might then be a doubt whether "the month of sowing of seed" more fitly described the spring sowing of seed in the twelfth month of a luni-solar year, counted from the *equinox*,—or the winter sowing of seed in the twelfth month of a luni-solar year, counted from the *solstice*. But when we find this twelfth month followed by a thirteenth, of which the especial and added epithet is *dark*, there can, as it seems to me, be little if any doubt that the winter month whose range in different years extended from 12th of December to 22nd January is better described by the epithet dark, than the rapidly brightening month whose range extended from 12th March to 22nd April.

Very curiously, then, and accurately does the Accadian calendar give us the date of its origin, and of the first naming of its months, as that when the *winter solstice coincided with the sun's entry into the first degree of the constellation Aries*[1] —the date in round numbers of 6,000 B.C.

To this same date it is, as I believe, that the miraculous protections accorded by the Aswins to the *distressed* solstitial sun and moon and earth appear to point, and fully does this view corroborate the opinion that the Aswin-legends took their rise in pre-Vedic times. They also,

[1] The winter solstice now coincides very closely with the sun's entry into Sagittarius. It *precedes* the sun's entry into Aries by almost a third of the whole circle of the ecliptic.

as do the Indra and Vritra myths, refer us for their origin to a more northern latitude than tropical India. In the tropics the sun is scarcely less powerful in winter than in summer. The astronomers who drew up the Accadian calendar, and the myth-makers of the Aswin-legends, must, according to the astronomic theory, have dwelt in temperate zones and formulated calendar and myths about 6,000 B.C.

VI

NOTES.—AHURA MAZDA, ETC.

[Ahura Mazda, a note reprinted from the *Proceedings of the Society of Biblical Archæology*, February 1900]

PROFESSOR HOMMEL in the March number for 1899 of these *Proceedings* calls attention in his *Assyriological Notes* to the name "Assara Mazas" appearing in a list of Assyrian gods. The section of the list in which this name appears contains "a number of foreign sounding names" belonging to gods honoured, presumably, in out-lying portions of the Assyrian dominions.

Professor Hommel claims "that this god (Assara Mazas) is no other than the Iranian Ahura Mazda," and he thus concludes his arguments in favour of this opinion—"concerning *Assara-mazas*, I should like to remark in closing this paragraph, that we have here the same older pronunciation of Iranian words as in the Kassitic *Surias*, 'sun' (later *Ahura* and *Hvarya*, but comp. Sanscrit *Asura* and *suria*), which is of the highest importance for the history of the Aryan languages. In the same Kassitic period, between 1,700 and 1,200 B.C., I suppose was borrowed by the Assyrians the Iranian god Assara-mazas."

In a Paper entitled *The Median Calendar and the Constellation Taurus*, printed in the June number for 1897 of these *Proceedings*, I made a very similar claim for the derivation of the name of the great god of the Assyrians—Assur.

The claim put forward was not based only on the resemblance in sound of "Assur" and "Ahura," but was in the first place founded on the virtual identity of the emblems of Assur and Ahura Mazda. For the *origin* of these emblems (referring as it was suggested they did to the Zodiacal constellation Sagittarius) a date as high as 4,000 B.C. was, on astronomic grounds, assumed, and it was pointed out that at that date there was no evidence of the existence of the Assyrian nation as a nation, nor any trace of a Semitic worship of the god Assur; whereas, on the other hand, as early as 3,800 B.C. there is evidence that a powerful Aryan race—the

Manda—rivalled the power, and threatened the Semitic rule of Sargon of Agane.

The opinion that the symbol of Ahura Mazda, and of Assur, was of ancient Aryan origin, naturally suggested the further thought that the *name* Assur, so closely resembling the earlier Indo-Iranian form Asura, of the Iranian Ahura, had, together with the emblem of the god, been borrowed from the Aryan ancestors of the Medo-Persians by the Semitic settlers who, early in the second millennium B.C., established themselves to the north of Babylonia. It may here be pointed out that no very certain Semitic derivation at present holds the field which the proposed Aryan derivation would occupy. According to some scholars it comes from a word signifying "a well-watered plain." According to Professor Hommel, the name Assur is derived from a word which originally meant "the heavenly host."

Professor Hommel, quoting as his authority the opinions of the Sanscrit scholar Oldenburg, and re-inforcing Oldenburg's opinions by arguments from other sources, further maintains the high probability of the Median god Ahura Mazda having been the representative of the Vedic Varuna, and also that Varuna was the moon.

Vedic scholars are divided in opinion as to what physical phenomenon is represented by Varuna. He is very generally supposed to personify "the vast extent of the encompassing sky," some say especially the sky at night-time—others claim him as a solar divinity, whilst Oldenburg, as we have seen, supposes him to be the moon. It is not to the question, however, what phenomenon Varuna represented, but to that of the probability or improbability of his original identity with the Median Ahura Mazda, that I would now draw attention.

It is said that "the parallel in character, though not in name, of the god Varuna is Ahura Mazda, the Wise Spirit." But a variety of considerations may lead us to entertain the possibility of a Vedic god other than Varuna being the parallel in character and in *epithet* of Ahura Mazda; a parallel which is also still more clearly to be recognized if we adopt the view, above contended for, of the identity of Assur, the *archer* god of Assyria, with Ahura Mazda.

The Vedic god Rudra is, like Varuna, an Asura

or Spirit. He is described as "the wise," and his votaries are encouraged to worship him "for a comprehensive and sound understanding." But in one passage the epithet "asura maha," so curiously recalling to our ears the name of the Avestan "Ahura Mazda," is actually applied to him.[1] As a wise and great Asura, Rudra seems to be as close a parallel to Ahura Mazda as Varuna; the resem-

[1] Wilson, *Rig Veda*, Maṇḍala ii., 1, 6. Uncertainty prevails among scholars as to the exact meaning to be given to the name Ahura Mazda. The Rev. L. H. Mills, D.D., under the heading "Zend," writes thus in *Chambers's Encyclopædia*: "The Supreme Deity Ahura Mazdâh, the Living God or 'Lord' (*ahu* = 'the living,' 'life,' or 'spirit'—root *ah* = 'to be'), the Great Creator (*maz* + *da* = Sansk. *mahâ* + *dhâ*), or 'the Wise One' (*cf.* *su-medhâs*)." Again, the same writer in his book on the Gàthàs, published in 1894, gives on p. 3 in his "verbatim translation," "O magnidonator (?) (vel) O Sapiens (?)," as alternative meanings for Mazda. Similar uncertainty seems to prevail as regards the meaning to be attached to the words of the passage in the Rig Veda to which reference has been made above, *i.e.*, Maṇḍala ii., Súkta i., verse 6. In Wilson's translation of the Rig Veda, vol. ii., p. 211, we read:—"Thou, Agni, art Rudra, the expeller (of foes) from the expanse of heaven": and in his note to this passage he says: "*Twam Rudro asuro maho divah*: *asura* is explained śatrúnám nirasitá, the expeller of enemies, *divas*, from heaven; or it may mean, the giver of strength. . . ." Macdonell (*Vedic Mythology*, p. 75) says that Rudra is called in this passage "the great *asura* of heaven."

blance of epithet in the case of Rudra makes the parallelism closer.

Varuna indeed in Vedic estimation held a much higher and more commanding position than Rudra, but considering how opposed the Avestan was to Vedic mythology on important points, we ought not to expect that the god elevated by the Medians above all others should have held a very exalted place amongst the Brahmins of India.

But it is when we turn our thoughts not only to Ahura Mazda but to his Assyrian representative Assur, that the parallelism between him and Rudra becomes more marked.

Rudra is not only a wise and great Asura, he is above everything else celebrated in the Rig Veda as an archer. He has "the sure arrow, the strong bow."[1] He is "the divine Rudra armed with the strong bow and fast flying arrows."[2]

In the Paper already referred to, it was suggested that an astronomic observation of the equinoctial colure passing through the constellations Sagittarius and Taurus was the probable origin of

[1] Wilson, *Rig Veda*, Maṇḍala v., x. (xlii.), 11.

[2] *Ib.*, Maṇḍala vii., xiii. (xlvi.), 1.

Median and (as derived from Median) Assyrian symbolism concerning Ahura Mazda and Assur. This observation could, as was pointed out, only have been made at the date, in round numbers, of 4,000 B.C.

It is a very tempting enterprise to seek in the mythologies of European nations for allusions to this same astronomic observation—an observation made, as we may believe, when the ancestors of the Iranian and Indian Aryans, and possibly the ancestors of the European nations, were still, if not all dwelling together, at least within easy intellectual touch of each other.

In Grecian fable we have the Centaur (the Bull-killer) Chiron giving his name to the constellation Sagittarius, and in this fable we may, as it would seem, find a better *astronomic* explanation of the term Bull-killer than that usually given concerning the well-mounted Thessalian hunters of wild cattle. The constellation Sagittarius, an archer, half man, half horse, is not a figure of Grecian invention. It is to be met with depicted on Babylonian monuments, unmistakably the archer of our celestial sphere; and this constellation, when it rises in the east, always drives below the western horizon—*i.e.*, mythically exterminates, the last stars of the constellation Taurus.

To Chiron, the chief Centaur, the epithet "wise" is especially given, and "he was renowned for his skill in hunting, medicine, music, gymnastics, and the art of prophecy"; of these not altogether congruous attributes Rudra the Vedic god possessed three of the most important. He was wise, he was an archer, and he was famed as "a chief physician among physicians."[1] In a verse, part of which has been already quoted,[2] worshippers are exhorted to "Praise him who has the sure arrow, the strong bow, who presides over all sanitary drugs; worship Rudra for a comprehensive and sound understanding, adore the powerful divinity with prostrations."

Apollo the far-darter, Artemis the goddess of the silver bow, also shared these same attributes, and Grecian legend would lead us to place them in the same part of the heavens as that allotted to Chiron—*i.e.*, Sagittarius. Apollo prompted Artemis to aim a shaft from her bow at a point on the

[1] Wilson, *Rig Veda*, Maṇḍala ii., xxxiii., 4.

[2] *Ib.*, Maṇḍala v., x. (xlii.), 11.

horizon, and this point was the head of the hunter Orion. Now the constellation Orion is exactly in opposition to the bow stars of Sagittarius; that the legend is astronomical is plainly to be inferred from its variant form, in which Artemis is represented as sending a Scorpion to sting Orion to death. The stars marking the Scorpion's sting are in very close proximity to the bow stars of Sagittarius.

Returning to Indian myths, the name of Siva does not occur in the Rig Veda; but in later Sanscrit works Siva is the representative of Rudra. In a hymn to Siva,[1] the following passages occur, and it is difficult to read them and not be reminded of the sculptured figures of Artemis, crescent-crowned and leading a stag by the horns. (Allowance must be made, however, for the tendency in Hindu art to multiply the heads, arms, and features of their gods.)

"I worship the great *Mahesa*, who shines like ten million suns: who is adorned with triple eyes: who is crowned with the moon: who is armed with

[1] Hymn to Siva, prefixed to "An Exposition of the Principles of Sanskrit Logic," by Bodhanundánath Swami, Calcutta.

the trident, the bow, the mace, the discus, the goad, and the noose :

Who is the eternal Lord ;

Who is bright as the snowy summit of Mount Kailâçe ; whose matted hair is ablaze with the crescent moon ;

. . . .

Whose hands hold the head of a deer and a battle-axe ;

Whose forehead is adorned with the bright half-moon ;

Whose fingers are interlaced to typify a deer ;

. . . ."

For the explanation of the Roman myths of Dianus and Diana (varying forms as the dictionary tells of Janus and Jana) we may naturally seek for the same astronomic origin, as for those concerning the Grecian archer divinities.

Janus indeed has not, so far as I know, ever been represented as an archer or a Centaur. The attribute for which he is especially renowned is that of "opener of the year," and this attribute, on the astronomic theory here proposed, would furnish the connecting link between the varying forms of the Italian deities above mentioned.

The many and still imperfectly understood changes that were made in the Roman year by successive rulers, have effaced the connexion of that year with the stars which must have originally presided over its opening. But Roman tradition embodied in Virgil's lines speaks of "the bright Bull" who "with his gilded horns opens the year."[1] The golden star-tipped horns of the Bull are as we know exactly opposed to the westernmost degrees of Sagittarius; and that constellation, in opposition to the sun, would therefore have marked the opening of just such a vernal year as that alluded to by Virgil. Whether this vernal year before the Julian reformation was still the calendrical year in Rome is, however, very doubtful.

Janus is represented with two heads, sometimes even with four, "to typify the seasons of the year." The *full moon* in Sagittarius 4,000 B.C. marked the season of the spring equinox—the sun then being in *conjunction* with the stars marking the horn tips of the Bull. The *new moon* in Sagittarius at the

[1] Virgil, *Georg.*, Lib. I., 217, 218.

same date marked the autumn equinox. The *half waning moon* in Sagittarius marked the season of the winter solstice: and the half moon of the *crescent or waxing moon* marked the season of the summer solstice. The four heads of Janus may thus have referred to the four seasons marked by the moon in Sagittarius.

The fact that the Indian archer Rudra (= Siva) and the Grecian archer Artemis, were represented as crowned by the *half*, not the *full moon*, would refer these myths to an Indo-Iranian, not to a somewhat later Iranian source. It was not to the reformed Iranian equinoctial year that they pointed, but to the sun's triumph at the solstitial season. In the Roman Janus myth we may rather detect the later Median influence, and suppose that it referred to a year beginning with the *full moon* in Sagittarius, a year opening in the spring, when the *sun* was in conjunction with the "gilded horns" of "the bright Bull."

All these mythological indications, derived from Median, Assyrian, Indian, and classical sources, though each of them looked at separately may not speak with much insistence, yet considered together seem to point us more and more clearly as we study them, to the fact that about 4,000 B.C. a very important and authoritative observation of the colures (amongst the Zodiacal constellations) was made, and that upon this observation much of the mythology of ancient nations was founded.

VII

ANCIENT INDIAN ASTRONOMY

[Reprinted from the *Proceedings of the Society of Biblical Archæology*, February 1900]

It is only on Talmudic authority, I think, that astronomy can be denied a place, and indeed an important place, in researches connected with Biblical Archæology.

On Talmudic authority we are told that, as a protest against the sun-, moon-, and star-worship of surrounding nations, the Hebrews were not permitted to calculate in any way beforehand, or by scientific methods based on the movements of the heavenly bodies, their days, their months, or their years.

The end of the day and beginning of the night could only be definitely ascertained when three stars were visible to the observer. The moon must have shown its pale sickle to some watcher of the heavens, before the first of the month could be announced. The beginning of the year, we are also told, was dependent on the earliness or lateness of the agricultural season, for three ears of corn, in a sufficiently advanced state of growth, were to be presented to the priest and waved before the Lord *on a fixed day of the first month* of the year.

This is what some passages of the Talmud [1]

[1] *Bible Educator*, edited by Rev. E. H. Plumptre, M.A., vol. iii. pp. 239 and 240. "It may have been with a view to render astrology impossible, that the Jews were forbidden to keep a calendar in the Holy Land, . . . as the length of the lunation, or lunar month, is, roughly speaking, twenty-nine days and a half, it is easy to know, from month to month, when to expect the crescent to become visible. Six times in the year the beginning of the month was decided by observation of the new moon. . . . On two months of the year the determination of the new moon was of such importance, that the witnesses who observed the crescent were authorized to profane the Sabbath by travelling to give information at Jerusalem. These occasions were the months Nisan and Tisri. . . . The Mishna records that on one occasion as many as forty pairs of witnesses thus arrived on the Sabbath at Lydda. Rabbi Akiba detained them, but was reproved for so doing by Rabbi Gamaliel. . . . . When the evidence was satisfactory, the judges declared the month to be commenced, and a beacon was lighted on Mount Olivet, from which the signal was repeated on mountain after mountain, until the whole country was aglow with fires."

seem to teach; but from Old Testament Scriptures, it is not possible to infer these calendrical restrictions with any degree of certainty. On the contrary, there is much in the Scriptures to lead us to an opposite conclusion.

On the very first page of the Bible we read of "the greater and the lesser lights," and of "the stars also" set in the heavens, to be "for signs, and for seasons, and for days and years." And scarcely have we turned this first page, when we meet the statement that "in process of time it came to pass, that Cain brought of the fruit of the ground an offering unto the Lord. And Abel, he also brought of the firstlings of his flock and of the fat thereof. And the Lord had respect unto Abel and to his offering." In the margin the words "in process of time" are rendered "at the end of days." In considering this passage we seem to be brought into touch with a definitely established year; and at once archæology and astronomy enter into the field of Biblical research, to tell us of a remotely old calendar—astronomic indications would date the origin of this calendar at about 6,000 B.C.—and from this calendar we learn that at "the end of days"—the end of the *dark* days of the year—there followed a month of "the sacrifice of righteousness": a sacrifice, we may well suppose, of the firstlings of the flock, as the stars in conjunction with the sun during this first month were imagined by the institutors of the calendar under the form of a lamb or ram ready for sacrifice.

To this calendrical first month our attention is again drawn when we read, in the book of Exodus, of the institution at God's command of the Hebrew festival, to be held on the 14th and 15th days of the month Abib.

This month Abib, it is generally assumed, is the equivalent of the month Nisan, spoken of in some of the later books of the Old Testament.

Astronomy and archæology again claim a hearing on this point. The month Nisan, the Semite equivalent of the Accadian month Bar ziggar (the month of the "sacrifice of righteousness"), we may gather from the evidence of the cuneiform tablets, had been the first month of a calendrical year in Babylon for many centuries—for millenniums, perhaps—before the date of Moses; and therefore archæology would teach us that the children of Israel were being recalled, from strange Egyptian modes of reckoning, to the observance of an ancient and patriarchal year and festival, when they were told that for them Abib was to be the first month of the year, and that on the 14th of that month, "a night to be much observed," they were to sacrifice of the firstlings of their flock, and were to hold the great festival of the Passover on the fifteenth day.

If "Abib," "Nisan," and "Bar zig-gar" are names used by various nations to designate one and the same month, Abib could not have been, as has very generally been supposed, a month varying according to the uncertain ripening of agricultural crops, and one taking its name from the *ears of corn* presented to the priest, and waved before the Lord on some fixed day of that month; but rather it must have been (as we know, from Babylonian sources that Nisan was) a well calculated soli-lunar and sidereal month. Now, if we adopt this view, we must find some alternative derivation for the month name Abib. Nor is it by any means difficult so to do.

On the fourteenth night of the first month—Bar zig-gar, Nisan, or Abib—"a night to be much observed," or rather, according to the marginal reading, "a night of observations"—the bright star Spica, which marks the *ears of corn* in the Virgin's hand, rose above the eastern horizon as the sun set in the west, and at midnight must have shone down brilliantly on the Hebrew hosts; for Spica is so bright a star, that even the beams of the full moon riding close at hand could not have obscured its lustre.

The Indians of to-day name their months from the stars in their lunar Zodiac which are in *opposition to*, not from those in *conjunction with*, the sun. The close resemblance of the Arab and Indian lunar Zodiacal series suggests the thought that the Arabs may have followed the same system of month *nomenclature* as the Indians; and if this were the case it would furnish a reason why Moses, who had so lately returned from his forty years' sojourn in Arabia, should—in recalling the Hebrews to the observance of such a year as that which was presumably followed by their forefathers Abraham, Isaac, and Jacob—have yet spoken of the first month of the year according to a *non-Babylonian* method of nomenclature, and should have called it Abib, after the star in *opposition to* the sun.

If now we adopt the opinion that an astronomic method of counting the year did in reality obtain amongst the Hebrews, a great difficulty must present itself to our minds in regard to the generally accepted theory that only on *a fixed day of the first month of the year* might the first reaped handful of corn be waved before the Lord.

The seasons in Palestine are not more punctual than in other countries. To restrict a husbandman to a fixed day of a year (even such a year as ours) before which he might not begin to put his sickle into the corn, would be felt as a hurtful and arbitrary regulation; but to restrict the husbandman to a fixed day in a luni-solar year would be a still more hurtful regulation. The beginning of a soli-lunar year may vary to the extent of a whole month. A late beginning of such a year might coincide with a very early agricultural season, and *vice versa* an early calendrical year might occur in a late agricultural season.

Considerations of this nature may incline us to inquire carefully whether the "generally accepted theory" (concerning the waving of the ears of corn before the Lord during the Passover week) rests upon Scriptural authority or on Talmudic and traditional teaching. As against an almost unbroken array of commentators, it is possible in this connexion to quote from the work of a learned Hebrew scholar a clearly expressed opinion that from the Scriptures themselves, it is not possible to infer directly a connexion in date between the waving of the first fruits and the Passover festival.[1]

[1] *Pentateuque*, Traduction Nouvelle, par Rabbi Wogue (Lazare), tom. 3. Discussing an important difference of opinion which exists amongst Jewish scholars and commentators as to the exact day of the Passover festival, on which the priest was to wave the sheaf before the Lord, the writer says: "Le texte porte: 'Le Lendemain du Sabbat,' indication qui a donné lieu à une dissidence importante entre les Pharisiens et les Saducéens. . . . Nous avons adopté le système talmudique, qui a pour lui l'autorité des Septante, des targoumîm, de Josephe, et l'usage immémorial de la Synagogue; mais, à ne consulter que les textes sans parti pris, nous ne souscririons à aucune des deux doctrines. Ni la cérémonie de l'ômer, ni le comput des semaines, ne sont mis par nos textes en rapport avec la Pâque, mais uniquement avec les moissons, soit ici, soit dans le Deutéronome (xvi. 9). Dès la récolte de l'orge, le divin Législateur veut qu'on lui fasse hommage des prémices de cette céréale; il n'indique point de date, parceque la moisson, pas plus que la vendange, et pas plus en Palestine qu'ailleurs, ne commence

But if our enquiries should lead us to accept, as at least a probability, the existence in Mosaic times of an astronomically counted Hebrew year, and if this admission should require us to change long-held opinions regarding the right observance of Hebrew festivals, on the other hand, the fact that we might then trace *Arabian* rather than *Babylonian* influence in the name of Abib would have its weight on the conservative side of the controversy concerning the post or pre-exilic *date* of the books of Exodus and Deuteronomy.

The fact that in India the months are named after the stars in opposition to the sun suggested the above proposed explanations of the Hebrew month name Abib as that of the month when the sun was in conjunction with the constellation Aries, and in opposition to the star Spica, marking the Zodiacal ears of corn. But there is a further point

à jour fixe. Mais une fois ouverte, elle se continue sans interruption; et comme les froments, en Palestine, sont coupés sept semaines après, les prémices du froment doivent être offertes au bout de sept semaines. L'Omer et la Pentecôte sont donc mobiles par exception, mais cette dernière est relativement fixe. Maintenant de quel 'Sabbat' est il question? Puisque tout ici est subordonné à *l'ouverture de la moisson*, ce sera naturellement le Sabbat qui suit cette ouverture."

of connexion to be observed between Indian astronomy and Biblical archæology, namely, that the *first month of the Indian year* is at the present date the month during which the sun is in conjunction with the constellation Aries. This month is called Chaitra, which is the Sanscrit name of the star Spica, and it is in fact the same sidereally marked month, which, according to the opinions here advocated, was the first month of the ancient Accadian, Babylonian, and Hebrew years.

It must, therefore, be a question of interest to Biblical students to determine, if possible, whether this Indian *first month* has only so been counted (as some scholars tell us) since about 570 A.D., or whether it has so been counted from the same remote time as was the Accadian month Bar zig-gar, that is, possibly, from about 6,000 B.C.

This question as to the month Chaitra forms part only of a larger controversy which has been long waged concerning the antiquity, or otherwise, of the whole science of astronomy in India.

To this larger controversy I have drawn attention in my Paper, *Astronomy in the Rig Veda*, read before the Congress of Orientalists assembled at Rome in 1899. In that Paper, arguments are put forward in support of the opinion that the Vedic bards possessed an acquaintance with the science of astronomy, and that much of the imagery of the hymns bore reference to the constellations of the Zodiac. For the gods Indra, Soma, Agni, and the Aswins, astronomic interpretations are proposed; and finally the question, which as it seems to me is one specially deserving the attention of the Society of Biblical Archæology—the question of the position of the month Chaitra as first month of the Indian year in Vedic and pre-Vedic times is discussed, and the claim that it was, and throughout remote ages had ever been, virtually the same month as the Accadian Bar zig-gar is insisted upon.

Pursuing further the controversy concerning the antiquity of astronomy amongst the Aryan races, in the note on "Ahura Mazda" (p. 152), I proposed an identification of the Vedic Rudra with the Median god—the god who presided over the Median equinoctial year, marked by observation of the full moon in the constellation Sagittarius.

Continuing then our enquiries into the astronomic myths of ancient India, let us turn our attention to the sons of Rudra—the *Maruts.* They are a group of gods very prominent among Vedic deities, and it is to be noted that Rudra is oftener alluded to in the Rig Veda as the father of the Maruts than in almost any other capacity. Now the Maruts—the stormy troop of Maruts—are celebrated as the companions and friends of Indra. They are "associated with him in innumerable passages." Here, at first sight, it might seem that the proposed astronomical identification of Indra and Rudra as solstitial and equinoctial personifications must break down; for how should the sons of the equinoctial Rudra always appear as the devoted companions of the solstitial Indra?

On further examination, however, a very interesting explanation of this difficulty presents itself. From a hymn (quoted at p. 157) to Siva, the Hindu representative of the Vedic Rudra, we learn that the crescent half-moon blazes on the forehead of Siva. Now the crescent half-moon, in the western degrees of the constellation Sagittarius, would, 4,500 B.C., have marked the month of the summer solstice; for the moon, in its "first quarter" in the first degrees of Sagittarius, must attain to "full moon" seven days later, either in the constellation Aquarius or Pisces, and the full moon in one or other of those two constellations marked the season of the summer solstice somewhat earlier than 4,000 B.C. The Maruts are often spoken of in the Veda as a troop, seven in number, or as seven troops of seven, or as three times seven in number. The astronomical thought therefore suggests itself, that the seven Maruts represent the seven days that elapsed between the crescent half-moon, blazing on the brow of Rudra, and the full moon of the summer solstice, or Soma pavamana—Soma purified in the celestial waters (see Plate XIII.). And this explanation of the Maruts does not contradict, but rather agrees with and includes the usual non-astronomic explanations held regarding them, namely, that they are *storm winds;* for we know that the days which accompany the setting in of the solstitial rainy season in India are the days in which the fierce tropical hurricanes or monsoons prevail.

Now let us turn from the Maruts to another, as

PLATE XIII.

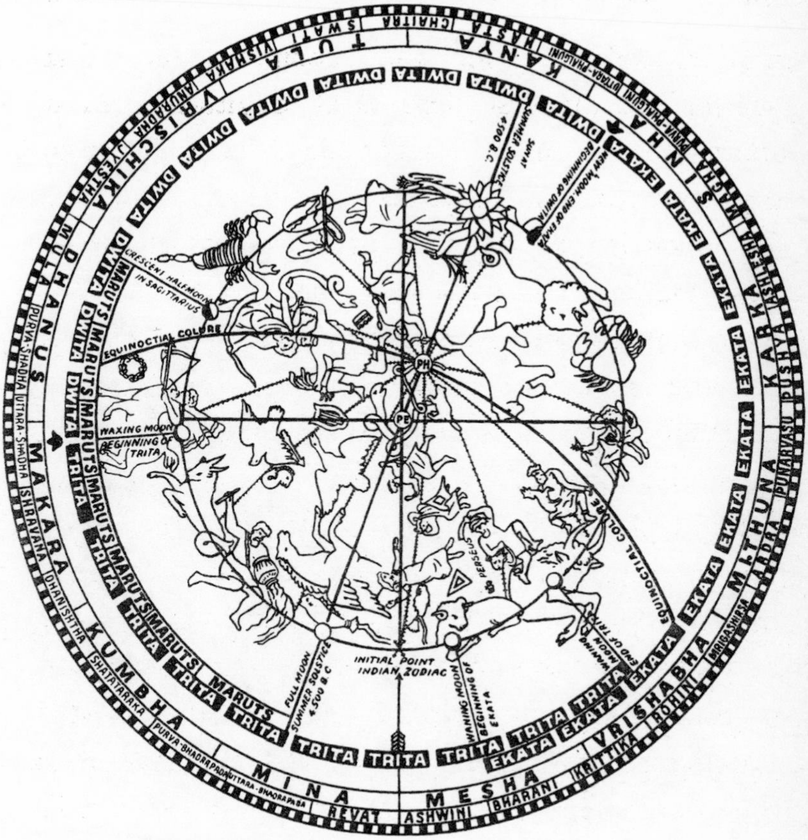

Outer circle divided into 360 degrees.

2nd circle. The names and extent of the twenty-seven Indian "Nakshatras" or divisions of the Lunar Zodiac.

3rd circle. Names and extent of the twelve Indian "Rashis" or divisions of the Solar Zodiac.

4th circle. Proposed three-fold division of the Vedic Lunar Month at Season of Summer Solstice.

Section of 5th circle. Proposed identification of "Maruts" with Moon's course through seven "Nakshatras" at Season of Summer Solstice.

The Constellations here appear as drawn on the celestial globe; they have not been reversed as in the other illustrations, hence an apparent, though not real, contradiction ensues.

[*To face p.* 174.

it seems to me, lunar and solstitial myth, namely, that of Trita Aptya.

Trita Aptya is a friend of the Maruts, and is said to have appeared on the same car with them. He is constantly, in the hymns, associated with Indra, and feats recorded in one passage as performed by Indra, are in another passage of the same hymn attributed to Trita.

Trita is also often spoken of together with Soma; and in the ninth Maṇḍala, again and again we read of the ten "maidens, or fingers," of Trita preparing the Soma juice for Indra.

All these attributes of Trita, and others to be mentioned later, are easily explainable on the astronomic theory already propounded in the identifications of Indra, of Soma, and of the Maruts.

In the name Trita there is certainly a suggestion of the number *three*, and Macdonell, in his *Vedic Mythology*,[1] brings proof to show "that it was felt to have the meaning of the third"—that is, in order of sequence.

But though the third, in this sense, does not

[1] P. 69.

actually carry with it the meaning of *third of a whole;* yet, to any one in search of an astronomical explanation of the Trita myth, the reiterated mention of the ten fingers of Trita quickly suggests the thought of a whole divided into three chief parts, each part containing ten lesser divisions —a whole therefore of thirty parts.

Now the lunar month—in reality consisting of twenty-nine and a half solar days (with some fractions over)—is in Hindu calendrical usage divided into thirty equal portions of time called "tithis," which are considered as lunar days; and here, as it would seem, we arrive at the physical basis of the Trita myth. Trita Aptya, or Trita in the waters (or of the waters), appears as the third part of the lunar month—the part during which the moon is to be seen in the celestial waters; and as Trita is so closely connected with Indra and Soma pavamana, that third part must have been the ten lunar days (five before and five after "the full") during which the moon is at its brightest, and in the constellation Aquarius.

If we think of Trita Aptya as a personification of the triumphant third of the moon's course through the constellations of the Zodiac at the season of the summer solstice (see Plate XIII.), and if we remember that the moon during the ten lunar days contained in that "third" came to its full in Aquarius or in Pisces, sometimes indeed at the juncture of these constellations, we shall be able to understand much of the figurative language of the Veda, which associates Trita with the stormy Maruts, with the victories of Indra over Vritra, and with the effulgence of Soma pavamana.

There is a legend concerning Trita not related but alluded to in the Rig Veda. This legend tells us that Trita was one of three brothers (Ekata, Dvita, and Trita), and that he was pushed into a well by his brothers, and over the mouth of the well a circular covering was placed with intent to keep Trita down and drown him. But through the circular covering the ever-triumphant Trita burst. Here there can be little doubt is a mythic description of the temporary disaster of eclipse overtaking the full moon of the summer solstice in the celestial waters of Aquarius or Pisces. The circular covering can be nothing else than the circular shadow of the earth covering the disc of the full moon, and Trita's triumph may well remind us of the serene victoriousness of the moon when it has emerged from eclipse and rides unharmed along the sky.

In the Zend Avesta Thrita corresponds in many points with the Vedic Trita. Thraetona also represents Trita under some of his other aspects, and mention is made of Thraetona's "two brothers who seek to slay him on the way."[1] From these facts it may be inferred that the Trita myth is pre-Vedic. We need not, therefore, be surprised to find traces of it in European mythologies. The name of Trita, with only a change of termination, appears as the Greek Triton, and we may guess at an allusion in the sculptured forms of Greek and Roman Tritons—half men and half fish—to the two watery constellations, Aquarius and Pisces, in which the Vedic Trita Aptya (son of waters) made his abode. The Roman rendering of these composite figures, especially, may recall to our minds the Zodiacal basis of the myth—the two fish of Pisces appearing in Italian art, as the two fish-tails

[1] Macdonell, *Vedic Mythology*, p. 69.

which terminate the human-headed figure of the Triton. Again Hecate, as has been pointed out by scholars, bears a close resemblance in name to Ekata. Hecate was a lunar divinity; she was worshipped and sacrificed to at the close of the month. We may therefore suppose she represented the waning moon. She is further said to have been the daughter of Perseus and Asteria. Looking at the figures of the celestial sphere (see Plate), we may trace the third part of the moon's course—the ten days of its waning appropriated to Ekata—and observe how this portion of its course began close to the *constellation Perseus.* Thus the Sanscrit Trita myth may explain the name and parentage of the Grecian Hecate.[1]

A study of ancient European calendars may, on the other hand, eke out our knowledge concerning the astronomic scheme in which Trita and his

[1] It is not to be supposed that only the month of the summer solstice was divided into the three parts, personified by Ekata, Dvita, and Trita: the legend of Trita Aptya, that is, Trita in the waters (or, of the waters), is necessarily restricted to that season in which the moon came to its full in the constellations Aquarius or Pisces. Some interesting indications in Indian and Greek mythology seem to point to a similar division of other months, but the subject is surrounded with uncertainties and difficulties.

brothers played such important parts. We read that in the Attic year "each month was divided into three decades," and the statement may confirm us in the opinion that, following an almost too mathematically imagined calendrical method, the ancestors of the Aryan race in remote ages counted their months, not as containing twenty-nine-and-a-half solar days, but as a portion of time containing three great equal divisions, the first, the second, and the third—Ekata, Dvita, Trita—each of these three parts being again subdivided into ten equal tithis. If this should have been the case, it would be interesting to note that the Greeks (and the Romans also, as shown by their cumbrous system of Kalends, Nones, and Ides) retained the plan of a threefold division of the months, but lost the originally concomitant arrangement of the ten equal divisions of each part into tithis, whence much difficulty ensued for Greeks and Romans alike in counting lunar months of alternately thirty and twenty-nine days. Indian astronomers, on the other hand, who retain the accurate and elaborate division of the month into equal tithis, must have long ago lost the thought of its originally threefold partition, for the Indians count each month as composed not of three periods of time, but of *a light and a dark half*.[1]

To one more lunar Vedic personage let us direct our attention: namely, to Atri—Atri who, unlike the conquering and ever-victorious Trita, is chiefly celebrated for his misfortunes. Agni, Indra, and especially the Aswins, moved by his misfortunes, come to the help of Atri, and by means of a hundred acts, a hundred devices, they extricate him from captivity, whether from a dark cavern or from a burning chasm. They make the time of his captivity even pleasant to him, giving him refreshing drink.

One of our own poets may help us to understand the Vedic metaphor of Atri's darksome cave. In the *Samson Agonistes* of Milton, the hero, describing his blindness, says—

> "The sun to me is dark
> And silent as the moon
> When she deserts the night,
> Hid in her vacant interlunar cave."

---

[1] "The Luni-Solar year is used for the regulation of festivals and domestic arrangements; it commences at present at the instant of conjunction of the Sun and Moon in the Sidereal month Chaitra. The Hindu Lunar months invariably consist of

Atri is, I believe, a personification of the *New Moon*, and thus we may understand how he is sometimes described as hidden in a dark cave, while at other times he is spoken of as in a fiery chasm, when the uppermost thought in the Vedic poet's mind is the close conjunction of the moon at that time with the burning sun. From his dark cave, or burning chasm, Atri is delivered by the "hundred acts" of worship and sacrifice which it was the custom in India, as in many other countries, to offer up at the time of New Moon, especially at the marked festivals of the winter and summer solstice, or the beginning of the calendrical year. On one occasion[1] we hear of

thirty Tithis, or Lunar days; and the whole month is divided into two equal parts of fifteen Tithis each, the one called Shukla or Shuddh Paksha—the bright half or increase of the Moon; the other Krishna or Vadya Pakṣha—the dark half or decrease of the Moon." (*The Indian Calendar* for the year 1892.)

[1] Wilson's *Rig Veda*, vol. iii. p. 297, *Maṇdala*, V. xl. "5. When, Súrya, the son of the *Asura* Swarbhánu overspread thee with darkness, the worlds were beheld like one bewildered, knowing not his place. 6. When, Indra, thou wast dissipating those illusions of Swarbhánu which were spread below the Sun, then Atri, by his fourth sacred prayer, discovered the Sun concealed by the darkness impeding his functions. 7. (Súrya speaks) Let not the violator, Atri, through hunger swallow with fearful (darkness) me who am thine; thou art Mitra,

Atri coming to the assistance of the sun, which had been hidden by the demon Swarbhānu. This darkening of the sun is generally understood to refer to a solar eclipse. A solar eclipse can only take place at the time of new moon. It is a little puzzling to find Atri, if Atri personifies the new moon, saving the sun from eclipse instead of being the cause of the disaster; but as in the Rig Veda Atri always appears as a friend, not an enemy, of the gods of light—Agni, Indra, and the Aswins—we may suppose that the Vedic bard chose to represent him as being present at, rather than causing the sun's eclipse. It may also be that a certain number of divisions of lunar time were considered as personified by Atri, and that an eclipse terminated in the third or fourth of those divisions; so that it could be said that Atri "by his fourth sacred prayer" discovered the sun. The passage is no doubt a difficult one;

whose wealth is truth; do thou and the royal Varuna both protect me. 8. Then the Brahman (Atri), applying the stones together, propitiating the gods with praise, and adoring them with reverence, placed the eye of Súrya in the sky; he dispersed the delusions of Swarbhánu. 9. The Sun, whom the *Asura*, Swarbhánu, had enveloped with darkness, the sons of Atri subsequently recovered; no others were able (to effect his release)."

still the fact that Atri was present at the eclipse of the sun seems to tell rather in favour of than against the supposition that Atri was a personification of the time of new moon.

The four astronomical interpretations here proposed for Rudra, the Maruts, Trita Aptya, and Atri, are all harmonious with and supplemental to the four discussed in my Paper read at Rome, and entitled *Astronomy in the Rig Veda*. They must to a great extent all stand or fall together. They have been very briefly stated, but if indeed an astronomic basis does, as suggested, underlie Vedic imagery, Sanscrit scholars, with the science of etymology at their command, will easily be able to follow up and pronounce upon the value of the clues here hazarded.

VIII

THE CHINESE CALENDAR, WITH SOME REMARKS WITH REFERENCE TO THAT OF THE CHALDEANS

[Reprinted from the *Proceedings of the Society of Biblical Archæology, December* 1901]

THE Chinese Lunar Zodiac is divided into 28 star groups named Siou. Gustav Schlegel in his *Uranographie Chinoise* having enumerated these 28 siou—or as he translates that term, "domiciles" —says : "La première chose qui nous frappe en voyant la liste des 28 domiciles, c'est qu'elle commence par le domicile *Kio*, ou la *Vierge*, preuve positive que c'était avec ce domicile que l'année a dû commencer primitivement,"[1] and further on he quotes from "le *Eul-ya* cette antique dictionnaire," as follows : "*L'Ancien des constellations*, c'est *Kio* et

[1] *Uranographie Chinoise*, p. 79.

Kang . . . ils sont les chefs des domiciles, et à cause de cela on les nomme *l'ancien des constellations:* et 'le signe d'Ancien des constellations' est exactement les domiciles *Kio* et *Kang*."[1] Schlegel adds: "Ce nom de *Ancien des constellations* répond exactement à celui de *Princeps Signorum* que les astrologues romains donnerent au *bélier;* à l'époque où cette constellation était signe de l'équinoxe du printemps. C'est-à-dire que le signe qui annoncait le commencement de l'année était le premier, le Princeps signorum, l'Ancien, le Chef, des constellations. Mais ces étoiles de la Vierge portent encore d'autres noms qui tous ont rapport au fait astronomique que l'astérisme *Kio* ouvrait l'année. Le 'Sing-king' les nomme les *Chefs des quatre régions*, les *Légions célestes. . . . Elles président aux métamorphoses de la création: elles sont traversées par l'écliptique et les sept clartés* (7 *planets*) *commencent* (*leur révolution*) *par elles.*"

The concluding words from the Sing-king which I have marked in italics—giving as they do the opinions held by ancient *Chinese* writers respecting the first divisions of their Lunar Zodiac — may

[1] *Uranographie Chinoise*, p. 87.

remind us of the opinions held by *Indian* astronomers as to their first division of the Zodiac.

In Whitney's comments on the *Sûrya Siddhânta* he observes :—" The initial point of the fixed Hindu sphere, from which longitudes are reckoned, *and at which the planetary motions are held by all schools of Hindu astronomy to have commenced at the creation*, is the end of the asterism Revatî, or the beginning of Açvinî."[1]

It is impossible to read of these two traditions concerning the initial point of the Chinese and of the Hindu ecliptic series of constellations, without suspecting some underlying cause common to both traditions.

The Chinese and Hindu initial points are diametrically opposite to each other on the ecliptic. Calendrically speaking, such opposite points may be taken to mark the same season and the same month —as for instance, in the old Accadian calendar the month names referred to the stars in *conjunction* with the sun. The month of the sacrifice of righteousness corresponded to the month during which the sun was in conjunction with the sacrificial Ram.

[1] V. p. 93.

This same month counted (theoretically) from the arrival of the sun at the end of Revati and beginning of Aswinī—the initial point of the Indian Zodiac—is in India called, after the star group in *opposition*, Chaitra.

Spica (α Virginis) is the chief star of the Nakshatra Chaitra, and Spica also is the chief star of the Chinese siou Kio, "l'astérisme," which, according to the tradition above recorded, "ouvrait l'année," and which (together with the neighbouring "siou Kang), président aux métamorphoses de la création," "sont traversées par l'écliptique, et les sept clartés commencent leur révolution par elles."

To any interested in the history of the Chinese calendar, or rather to any interested in the history of the human race, the question as to the reason for the choice of this point and for the equal honour in which it was held (as we have seen) by the Accadian, the Hindu, and the Chinese nations, is a question worthy of close attention.

In former Papers contributed to these *Proceedings*, I have drawn attention to the many indications in ancient cuneiform and Indian literature, which seem to point to the conclusion that about 6,000 B.C., in some part of Asia and in a latitude probably as far north as 40 degrees, a calendar was instituted by "some ancient race of men," that this calendar dealt with a year beginning at the season of the *winter solstice*, and that the stars which at that date were chosen to mark the solstitial year were those in the first degrees of the constellation Aries in *conjunction* with—and the bright star Spica in *opposition* to—the sun. I suggested that the Accadians and later Babylonians, as also the Aryans of India, continued to follow as star-marks for their years the constellations chosen by the institutors of this ancient calendar, and that therefore in the course of ages the beginning of the years of these peoples moved gradually away from the season of the *winter solstice*, approaching always nearer to the *vernal equinox*, close to which point we find it "bound" at the time of the fall of the Babylonian power; while in India, where the star-mark Spica is still followed, the year now begins about twenty days after the spring equinox.

Indications in Mesopotamian and Indian literature have seemed to me to point to the above conclusions. The opposed view, held by most writers on the subject, is that only at the late date (about the beginning of our era) when the stars of Aries in conjunction, and the star of Spica in opposition, marked the *equinoctial* season, were they adopted as marks for the beginning of the year by Babylonians and Hindus respectively.

I think that the position held by the star Spica in Chinese ancient astronomical tradition may be claimed as telling strongly in favour of an originally *solstitial* as opposed to an originally *equinoctial* beginning of the sidereal years of the Accadian, Hindu, and Chinese nations, for never has the claim been made that the *Chinese* years were counted from the vernal equinox; but on the contrary the opinion has been very generally held and expressed by Chinese scholars that at some remote date the new year's festival was held in China at the season of the winter solstice.

Gustav Schlegel, one of the latest writers on the subject of Chinese astronomy, though he admits that, "selon l'opinion générale l'année chinoise commence toujours avec le solstice d'hiver," has put forward a view entirely opposed to this generally held opinion: according to his theory, the

Chinese have from the most remote times counted their years, as they count them at present—*i.e.*, from the new moon nearest to *the season mid-way between the winter solstice and the spring equinox:* and as he is convinced—as we have seen—that the beginning of the Chinese year was originally marked by the asterism Kio, he demands as the lowest possible date for this origin of the Chinese calendar, that of 16,916 B.C., when the constellation Kio marked, by its heliacal rising, the mid-season between solstice and equinox.

Schlegel brings forward many learned and ingenious arguments drawn from Chinese literature to support this theory. It would be impossible at second hand, and in a small space, to state fairly his arguments with a view to rebutting them. His volumes are full of valuable information concerning the "Uranographie Chinoise," but it has not seemed to me when reading and re-reading his work, that the grounds on which he relies are sufficiently established to support the high claims to antiquity which he puts forward for the origin of the modern Chinese method of counting the year from the mid-season between solstice and equinox.

It has on the contrary seemed to me that on historical grounds a theory may be arrived at which will furnish a reasonable explanation of the present somewhat exceptional Chinese calendrical methods, and which will, if it is accepted, strongly reinforce the grounds for holding the already general opinion that the year in ancient times in China was solstitial. That opinion once established must lead us with increased confidence to attribute the honour traditionally paid by Hindus and Chinese alike to the initial point of their respective ecliptic series of star groups to, as I have said, their common acquaintance with a calendar established on high authority at the date in round numbers of 6,000 B.C.

The year in China is luni-solar, and it is, as has been pointed out, counted from the season exactly midway between the winter solstice and the spring equinox.

It is counted from this mid-season and not from the sun's opposition to, or conjunction with, any particular star or star group. It is therefore not a *sidereal* but a *tropical* year; and it is estimated at exactly the same length as is our European Gregorian year.

We here in Europe are not yet tired of congratulating ourselves on the scientific success attained by Pope Gregory XIII., when in 1582 he, with the help of many learned men and astronomers, established, as a reform of the earlier Julian calendar, a method of securely binding all recurring anniversaries—civil and ecclesiastical—to the exact same *season* of the year.

Calculations for the arrangement of the Julian calendar had strained the scientific powers of the astronomers of Greece and Rome in Cæsar's time, but the length of the year estimated by them was twelve minutes greater than that arrived at by the astronomers of Gregory's later date.

To find, as we do, in the far east of Asia a people counting the length of their luni-solar year with the same accurate exactness as that only attained to as late as 1582 A.D. in Europe, might well cause us surprise, were it not that history furnishes us with an easy explanation of this exact identity of Chinese and European calendrical calculations, by teaching us that the calendar by which the Chinese now count their years, and by which they have counted them for nearly three hundred years, was really compiled at Peking by Roman ecclesiastics, to whom the Gregorian methods were well known, and for whom, indeed, the study of these methods must have possessed the charm of novelty added to its intrinsic utility and scientific interest.

Two learned Jesuit Fathers obtained in the 17th century great influence at the Chinese Court. In 1600 A.D., Matteo Ricci was allowed with his companions to settle at Peking, where he spent the remainder of his life in teaching mathematics and other sciences.

In 1610, Johann Adam von Schall, another learned Jesuit Father, "was sent out partly in consequence of his knowledge of mathematics and astronomy to China," and was ultimately "invited to the Imperial Court at Peking, where *he was entrusted with the reformation of the calendar* and the direction of the public mathematical school."[1]

Under these circumstances, when we read that "according to the Chinese work, *Wan-nian-shu*, or 'Ten thousand-year Calendar,' in which the ele-

[1] *Chambers's Encyclopædia*, 1901.

ments of the Chinese calendar from 1624 A.D. until 1921 A.D. are calculated by the Astronomical Board at Peking, the earliest date of the Chinese New Year's Day is January 21st, and the latest February 20th"[1] —when we read this and remember that Johann Adam von Schall was in 1624 in charge of the reformation of the calendar at Peking, we need feel no surprise to find "the elements of the Chinese calendar" calculated in advance for 279 tropical, that is Gregorian, years. Indeed the influence of the European ecclesiastic in these calculations is clearly to be recognized in their very form, for we are easily reminded by it of the "Table to find Easter from the present time to—such and such a year—A.D. inclusive," prefixed to our English Books of Common Prayer. And we may be tempted to smile when we see the jealously conservative Chinese nation so peaceably—perhaps unwittingly—accepting a reformation of their calendar at the hands of foreigners, and contrast with this acceptance the turbulent opposition with which for so

[1] *On Chronology and the Construction of the Calendar, with special regard to the Chinese Computation of Time compared with the European.* By Dr. K. Fritsche.

long the introduction of the Gregorian calendar into many European countries was resisted.

It may well be that the Jesuit Fathers to whom the Emperor entrusted the reformation of the calendar were themselves not aware of the magnitude of the reformation they were introducing into Chinese methods, for they found the luni-solar festival of the new year, as we may learn from the Chinese literature of that date, occurring close to that *season* to which they then so scientifically bound it. But, according to the theory which in this Paper I am anxious to advocate, this *season* midway between solstice and equinox had not been chosen with definite intention as the first of the year by the Chinese, but had only been arrived at, in consequence of an age-long following on their part of a star group, chosen thousands of years earlier, by one of their ancient emperors, as that from which the beginning of their year was to be counted. This star group was the Siou (domicile) Hiu, the eleventh division of their Lunar Zodiac, and it is marked by the stars β Aquarii and α Equulei. (See diagram.)[1]

[1] The 28 Siou are not of equal extent, and there are many discrepancies in the Chinese tables which profess to give the

There is in the great History of China a description given of a reformation of the calendar carried out by the Emperor Tchuen-Hio, whose date is placed at 2510-2431 B.C. The conjunction of the sun and moon close to the Siou Hiu is in this description clearly referred to as a mark given for the beginning of the year. But the fact of this choice of the star mark Hiu has, for European scholars, been obscured by a most unfortunate paraphrase made use of by Père de Mailla, the translator into French of the *Histoire Générale de la Chine.* He gives us in the passage describing Tchuen-Hio's reformation the phrase, "15° du Verseau," instead of the Chinese expression, "the Siou Hiu."[1]

The Siou Hiu extends over some eight or ten

number of degrees attributed to each. In the diagram, therefore, only the stars which compose the three adjoining domiciles, Niu, Hiu, and Wei are noted, and they are connected by straight lines, according to Chinese astronomical custom.

[1] The fact that P. de Mailla has so paraphrased the Chinese original has thus plainly been attested by the late Professor Legge. In answer to a question addressed to him on the subject, he wrote, in December 1894, to Mr. H. W. Greene, Fellow of Magdalen College, Oxford, as follows: "In the passage from P. de Mailla's History, that writer is both translating and paraphrasing 'the star group Hiu.'"

PLATE XIV.

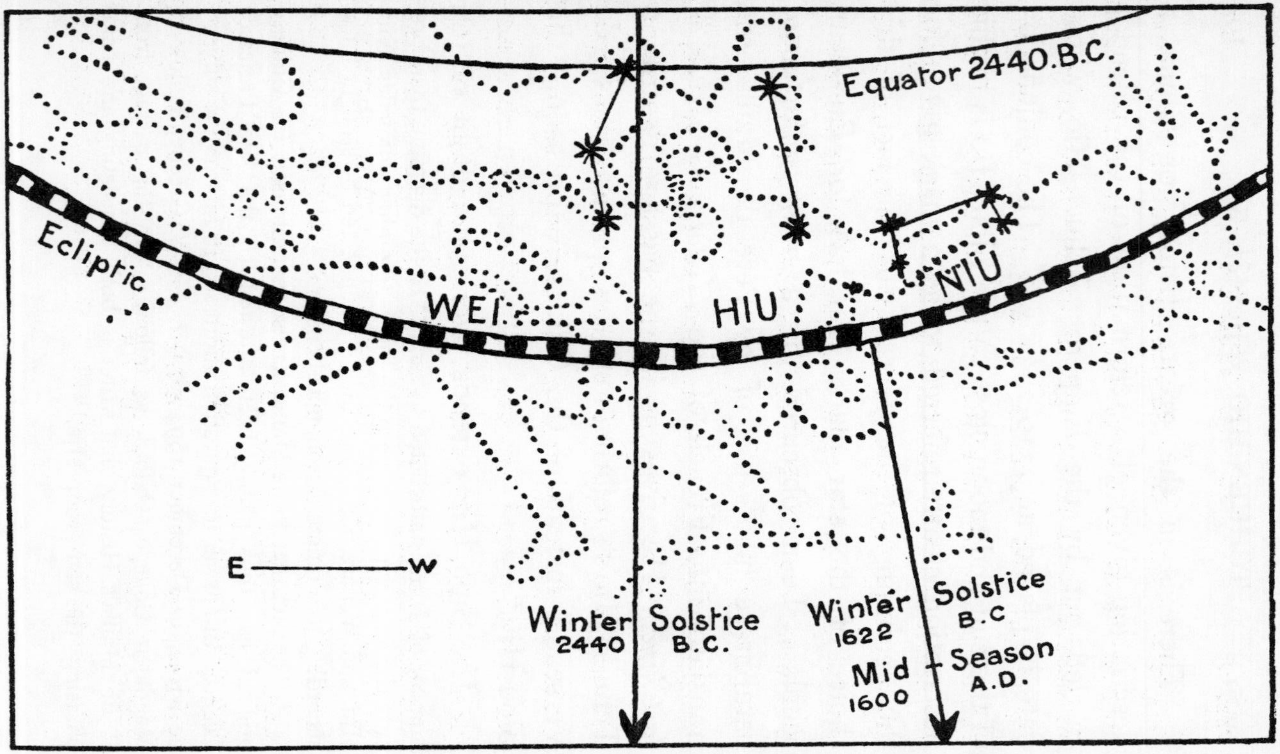

Domiciles Niu, Hiu and Wei, of the Chinese Lunar Zodiac.

degrees of the ecliptic in the constellation Aquarius; to restrict to *one* degree the given star mark was an inaccuracy serious enough in an astronomical statement, but this inaccuracy is as nothing when compared with the further entire distortion of facts occasioned by P. de Mailla's use of the ambiguous phrase, "15° du Verseau," ambiguous because it can be taken to refer either to the fifteenth degree of the *sign*, or of the *constellation* "du Verseau" (Aquarius).

The Siou Hiu is situated, as stated above, in the *constellation* Aquarius (see diagram), but astronomers reading P. de Mailla's translation have understood the phrase in its technical sense, and have therefore been led to believe that the Emperor Tchuen-Hio fixed the beginning of the Chinese year to the 15° of the *sign* Aquarius; and as, astronomically and technically speaking, the 15° Aquarius (sign) has no reference to any star or constellation, but is only that point of the ecliptic to which the sun attains exactly at the mid-season between winter solstice and spring equinox, they have taken for granted that 2,500 B.C. the Chinese year began at that point, and therefore at the same season as it does at the present time.

But as we now learn on the high authority of Professor Legge that it was to the *star group Hiu* that Tchuen-Hio is recorded to have bound the beginning of the year, we know that if the record is true, the year in Tchuen-Hio's time must have begun at the *winter solstice*, and not at the *mid-season*, between it and the equinox.

When due correction of P. de Mailla's paraphrase has been made in the passage recording Tchuen-Hio's reform, there remains still a difficulty to be overcome in the account of this event given in the *Histoire Générale de la Chine*, or rather I should say that it is when we have corrected P. de Mailla's paraphrase that this difficulty appears. For in the history it is stated that it was from the new moon at the beginning of spring, and near to the star group Hiu, that the year was then and henceforth to be counted, and this statement contains an astronomical contradiction. Our knowledge of the precession of the equinoxes teaches us that the star group Hiu in Tchuen-Hio's time did not mark the *beginning of spring*, but rather the very *middle of winter*.

Unless, then, we throw aside as worthless the whole record of Tchuen-Hio's reform of the calendar, we are driven to suppose that some Chinese historian, ignorant of the precession of the equinoxes, and writing at a date when, owing to that precession, the first new moon of spring was indeed close to the star group Hiu, and that of the winter solstice far distant from it—that this historian made what he may well have considered a necessary correction in the record with which he was dealing, and substituted the "first day of spring" for the "mid-winter season." Nor need we much blame him for making such a correction, when we find ourselves driven by stress of modern enlightenment to correct his correction, and to read "mid-winter" where he has written "beginning of spring."

Let us now read with due corrections, between square brackets, the record of Tchuen-Hio's reformation of the calendar as given in the *Histoire Générale de la Chine*.

"Tchuen-Hio . . . profitant de la paix dont jouissoit l'empire, transféra sa cour à Kao-yang. Ce fut dans cette ville, que toujours passionné pour

la connoissance des astres, il établit une espèce d'académie, composée des Lettrés les plus habiles en cette science. On recueillit toutes les observations anciennes qu'on compara avec les modernes, et on poussa l'astronomie à un degré de perfection surprenant. Les règles sûres qu'ils établirent pour supputer les mouvements du soleil, de la lune, des planettes, et des étoiles fixes, acquirent à Tchuen-Hio le titre glorieux de restaurateur, et même de fondateur de la vraie astronomie. C'est une perte que ces règles ne soient pas venues jusqu' à nous.

"Après plusieurs années de travail, Tchuen-Hio détermina qu'à l'avenir l'année commenceroit à la lune la plus proche du premier jour du printems [proche du solstice d'hiver] qui vient vers le 15° du *Verseau;* [vers le Siou Hiu] et comme il savoit par le calcul qu'il en avoit fait, que dans une des années de son règne les planettes devoient se joindre dans la constellation *Che* (constellation qui occupe 17° dans le ciel, dont le milieu est vers le 6° des *Poissons*) il choisit cette année-là pour la première de son calendrier, d'autant plus que cette même année le soleil et la lune se trouvoient en conjonction, le

premier jour du printems [le jour du solstice d'hiver]."[1]

It may, of course, be objected to the proposed correction of the *season* in this passage as follows: granting that either the star mark Hiu, or the *spring season* said to have been chosen by Tchuen-Hio, must have been erroneously recorded in the *Histoire Générale*, the probabilities are equal as to which element in the statement is or is not true. Tchuen-Hio may have chosen the moon nearest to the first day of spring, and may have named some constellation other than Hiu near to which this first moon was in conjunction with the sun. The late Chinese historian, instead of tampering as above supposed with the recorded *season*, may have substituted the name of the star group Hiu, which at his date marked the beginning of spring, for that "other" chosen by Tchuen-Hio.

But the probabilities on this point are in reality not equally balanced. For, in the first instance, we must take into consideration the very general opinion that the year in China anciently began at the winter solstice, and the fact that this season was in Tchuen-

[1] Vol. I. p. 33.

Hio's time so accurately marked by the junction of the star groups Wei and Hiu (see diagram), and we must further take into consideration the many references to the star group Hiu in ancient Chinese literature, which connect it very specially with traditions concerning the Emperor Tchuen-Hio. Many passages in the works of the Père Gaubil are to be met with to this effect, as for instance where he thus quotes and comments on a statement in the Eul-ya. "On désigne *Hiuen-hiao* par la Constellation Hui (*sic*); on appelle encore ce Signe *Tchouen-Hio.*" Gaubil adds, "Le Signe Hiuen-Hiao est celui que nous appelons Amphora. Le dictionnaire [Eul-ya] met dans ce Signe la Constellation *Hiu;* c'est-à-dire que le Signe commençoit par quelque dégré de cette Constellation. L'Histoire Chinoise asseure que l'eau est le symbole du régne de Tchouen-Hiu (*sic*). L'Eul-ya dit formellement que Hiuen-hiao Signe Celeste du Zodiaque désigne l'Empereur *Tchouen-Hiu* (*sic*)."[1] Schlegel also tells us that the Chinese placed the soul of Tchuen-Hio in the constellation Hiu.

[1] *Observations Mathématiques, Astronomiques,* &c., redigées et publiées par le P. Étienne Souciet, tome iii. pp. 31–33.

But not only is Hiu in Chinese literature closely associated with the Emperor Tchuen-Hio: it is also closely bracketed with the season of the winter solstice. Schlegel gives many quotations to this effect from Chinese authorities, but he would refer all such allusions to the far back time between 14,000 and 13,000 B.C., when Hiu was in opposition to the sun at that season, not in conjunction with it as at Tchuen-Hio's date.

Of Hiu he writes:—

Hiu, ou Tertre funéraire.[1]

"C'est cet astérisme dont la culmination à l'heure *tsze* (11^h de la nuit) annonçait le solstice d'hiver. . . . 'Au solstice d'hiver,' dit le Mémoire sur la divination par la tortue, 'la course du soleil et des astres n'est pas encore complète, et ils sont conséquemment délaissés comme des orphelins (*Kou*) et vides (*Hiu*).' Le solstice d'hiver était donc considéré par les Chinois comme la position d'un 'orphelin au tombeau de ses parents.' . . . Le père Noël à traduit (*Hiu*) par Vacuum, Vide; mais nous préférons traduire litéralement par Tertre funéraire."[2]

[1] *Uranographie Chinoise*, p. 214.
[2] *Ibid.* p. 217.

Taking these various passages into consideration, we are, I think, led to feel that the probabilities in favour of Tchuen-Hio having chosen the star group Hiu to mark, in conjunction with the sun, the winter solstice, are greater than those in favour of a comparatively modern choice of that star group as a mark for the beginning of spring.

Reading the passage of the *Histoire Générale* as corrected above, we may assume that Tchuen-Hio intended to establish sure rules by which the Chinese were for the future to count their years from the *solstice*, and from the conjunction of sun and moon close to the star group Hiu. But we also know that the following of these sure rules was an impossibility. Either the season or the star mark must in the long course of ages have been abandoned. It would be a difficult, perhaps an impossible, task to ascertain how far, or in what manner, the attempt was made under successive dynasties to carry out the injunctions of Tchuen-Hio. We read in the *Confucian Analects* that in answer to his "disciple," who had asked him, "how the government of a country should be administered," the Master said—as the first of five rules—"Follow the seasons of

Hsiâ." And in his note on this text the commentator says, "Confucius approved the rule of the Hsiâ dynasty. His decision has been the law of all the dynasties since the Ch'in."[1] During all the centuries in which the Hea or Hsiâ dynasty held sway, *i.e.*, from 2205 to 1766 B.C., the sure rules of Tchuen-Hio might have been carried out without much difficulty, for at the *new moon nearest to the winter solstice* the sun would still have been in or *near to the constellation Hiu* (see diagram), though at the date of Confucius, 551–479 B.C., this was no longer the case. Judging from the final result, we may, I think, take it for granted that the Chinese followed the *star mark* and not the *season* appointed for the beginning of the year by Tchuen-Hio. And thus following the star mark, the beginning of their year imperceptibly receded from the solstice, and approached the spring equinox, so that in 1600 A.D. the Jesuit fathers found the year still beginning at the new moon, "vers le Siou Hiu," *and hence at the season midway between the winter solstice and the spring equinox.*

[1] Legge, *Chinese Classics*, vol. i., *Confucian Analects*, book xv., ch. x.

In a former Paper contributed to these *Proceedings*,[1] I suggested that in the inscription engraved on Gudea's diorite statue we had evidence of a reform of the already existing Accadian calendar—in use from a date much earlier than Gudea's in the neighbouring Babylonian kingdom.

Gudea's date is placed by scholars at about 2800 B.C.—not much earlier than at that claimed in the Chinese History for Tchuen-Hio.

Much honour is given by this priestly ruler of Lagash "to Ningirsu, and to the goddess Bau, his beloved consort," and the concluding lines of the inscription run as follows :—

"On the day of the beginning of the year, the day of the festival of Bau, on which offerings were made: one calf, one fat sheep, three lambs, six full grown sheep, two rams, seven *pat* of dates, seven *sab* of cream, seven palm buds.

"Such were the offerings made to the goddess Bau, in the ancient temple on that day."

The generally received opinion as to Ningirsu (Ninib) is, that he was the god of the "southern sun"; and, as I contended in my Paper, the *southern*

[1] February 1896, V. p. 54.

sun, if we think of the sun in its *yearly*, not merely in its daily course, may fitly represent the sun of the winter solstice, while the goddess Bau=Gula is the goddess by whose very name the constellation Aquarius, as we may assume, was designated in the Accadian astrological texts.

If from Gudea's inscription concerning the new year's festival a reform in the calendar of Lagash may be inferred, by which the beginning of the year was transferred from the stars of Aries to those of Aquarius, we should find that the Lagash inscription, and the great History of China, tell us the same story—the Lagash inscription supplementing the Chinese History in this important point—that whereas the account of Tchuen-Hio's reform has been manifestly more or less garbled in its long descent through human hands: that of Gudea's new year's festival is a contemporaneous and utterly untampered-with account. It is also of some moment to note one curious point of resemblance in the idea connected with the stars of Aquarius, by the astronomers of countries so far distant from each other as China and Mesopotamia. Hiu, as we have learnt, may be translated as "Vacuum," and the name of the goddess Bau or Bahu bears the same signification as the Hebrew word translated in Genesis i. 2 by "void."[1]

If we now accept Tchuen-Hio's reformation as a re-adjustment of a previously-existing sidereal and originally solstitial calendar, we are at once given the clue to the two so similar Hindu and Chinese traditions quoted above, concerning the initial point of their Lunar Zodiacs: and we shall recognise that Kio—containing the star Spica—*in opposition to*, and the first degrees of Aswinī, *in conjunction with*, the sun, obtained the posts of leaders of the lunar series for the same reason—namely, *that they marked the beginning of the year at the winter solstice* 6000 B.C.

To this same cause I have here, and elsewhere, attributed the fact that in the Accadian calendar the stars of Aries held the same position, and marked the *first* month of the year, as the month of the "sacrifice of righteousness."

In thus tracing back the history of the calendars of the ancient nations of the East, in observing the

[1] Sayce, *Transactions of the Society of Biblical Archæology*, February 1874.

identity of their earliest astronomical traditions, and noting the curious points of contact and divergence in their later scientific and mythological ideas, the impression seems to force itself upon us more and more definitely, that before the races of mankind were "scattered abroad upon the face of the whole earth," their ancestors were capable of great scientific achievements, and possessed in common high intellectual aspirations.

We in these later days, so picturing to ourselves the past, may be freshly struck by the words of the ancient history, which tell us of the time when "the whole earth was of one language and of one speech."

PART II

PLATES.

PART II.

PLATES XV., XVI., XVII., AND XVIII.

IN the foregoing pages arguments have been urged in support of the view that the ecliptic circle, at the remote date (speaking in round numbers) of 6000 B.C., had been portioned by some "ancient race of men" into twelve divisions; and that the twelve constellational figures of the Zodiac had then also been imagined under forms more or less closely resembling those which we recognize in the heavens at the present day.

Most of the arguments in favour of this opinion are necessarily based on considerations connected with the phenomena of the heavens, effected in the long course of ages by a slow revolution of the earth's axis. Astronomers during the last two thousand years have carefully observed the effects and studied the causes of this slow terrestrial movement, and they can now tell us with confidence and exactness that the space of 25,868 years is required for the accomplishment of one such revolution of the earth's axis.

In our enquiry into the astronomy of the ancients we need not at all turn our minds to the difficult subject of the causes, or indeed even to the fact, of this slow movement of the earth's axis, further than to realize fully that its effects have been to produce a slow but continuous change in the apparent position of the fixed stars, a change not in their position relatively to each other, but in their distances from the heavenly equator and its poles.

The effort to fully realize these effects by means of careful calculations and measurements must prove to any but an astronomer a most arduous task; but, by aid of the mechanical contrivance called a "precessional globe," much of the difficulty of the task may be overcome. The accompanying diagrams have been drawn from a precessional globe, which can be adjusted so as to show the position of the poles and equator amongst the fixed stars, at dates distant from each other by intervals of 538 years.[1]

I have shown in continuous outline those constellations for whose first imagining it seemed to me as early a date might be claimed as that referred to in each diagram; all others are given in dotted outline. The strange figures of the "ancient constellations" are here drawn as they are represented on the globe; but the fixed stars which mark these figures for observers of the heavens, I have not ventured to indicate, as to do so would have required great accuracy of drawing and measurement. It is not for a moment to be contended that all the ancient constellations were imagined *exactly* under the forms by which we have learnt to know them from classic representations, from the poem of Aratos, and from the star list of Ptolemy. Variants of many of the figures are to be met with in astronomical atlases and on the celestial globes in use to-day; and to establish the relative claims concerning the antiquity of these variant forms is a branch to itself of research.

That these constellations have indeed been well denominated "ancient" is scarcely to be denied, and our only wonder, when studying the subject, must be, not that some differences are to be met with as to the exact form under which, at different dates and by different nations, these figures were delineated in the heavens, but rather the wonder must be that (as archæological research is always more and more clearly establishing) through many thousands of years, and by nations long and widely separated, the stars, which to an unaccustomed observer seem to be scattered in wild and random profusion on the sky, should have

[1] 1800 A.D. is the date to which the globe in question originally refers; the intervals of 538 years can be reckoned backwards or forwards from this date.

been divided into the same distinct groups, and thought of as representing the same mysterious beings.

But though it may be impossible to maintain that the Grecians have handed down to us in an absolutely unchanged form the figures of the ancient constellations as they were first imagined in remote ages, yet many proofs may be cited in favour of the opinion, that not lightly or arbitrarily did astronomical artists venture to tamper with the Zodiacal and extra-Zodiacal figures.

Some of these proofs have already been pointed out in the foregoing Papers. Attention will be drawn to others in the consideration of the diagrams here given.

In Plates XV., XVI., XVII., and XVIII., the positions of the solstitial and equinoctial colures amongst the constellations are given at the date 5744 B.C. Had it been possible, I should have liked to have drawn these diagrams as at 6000 B.C.—not only because it is easier to deal with and to remember a round number such as that, but also because at that date the solstitial colure passed through the ecliptic only one degree distant from the initial point of the Indian Zodiac—a point which there seems good reason to believe was the initial point of many, other than Indian, ancient Zodiacs.

Owing to the mechanical restrictions of the precessional globe, it was not possible to adjust it to any more accurate date than that of 5744 B.C.

It will not be necessary here to reiterate the considerations in favour of the opinion already advanced that the calendrical importance of the constellation Aries in some nations, and its symbolical importance in the mythology of others, may best be explained by the supposition that the choice of this constellation as "Prince and Leader" of the signs was made *not* when its stars marked the spring equinox, but when they marked the winter solstice.

Let us rather take this opinion as a working hypothesis, and turn our attention to the importance, in ancient symbolism, of the *four* constellations—Aries, Cancer, Libra, and Capricornus—which, according to this hypothesis, marked the *four* seasons, and the cardinal points 6000 B.C.

Next in this order to Aries comes Cancer, *The Crab* (see Plate XVI.). In Babylonia, it seems to be established that a *tortoise*, not a crab, represented the fourth constellation of the Zodiac. In Egypt, as we learn from the Zodiacs of Esneh and Denderah, it was the *scarabæus* beetle that held the place given to the crab in the Grecian sphere.

There is a sort of outward resemblance between these three creatures, wide apart as they are anatomically from each other. They are all hard-shelled, creeping, and insignificant-looking animals. Why under any of these three forms a constellation of the Zodiac should have been depicted, it is difficult to conjecture; but if we have to admit that in Egyptian astronomy the beetle played the important part of marking as a constellation one of the quarters of the ecliptic circle, this admission will furnish us with an adequate reason for the extraordinary honour paid in Egyptian symbolic art to this lowly, and in itself unattractive, insect.

The scarabæus, according to our hypothesis, marked in ancient calendrical tradition the spring equinox when in *conjunction* with the sun, and the autumn equinox in *opposition* to it. And it was as presiding *visibly in opposition* that we may reasonably suppose it gained such honour in Egypt. For the autumn, not the spring, is in that land the time when vegetation begins to burst into life, and when all Egypt rejoices. I think, moreover, that facts connected with the worship of the Apis Bull will further strengthen the opinion that the Egyptians considered the constellations in *opposition* to the sun to be those which presided over particular seasons and months.[1]

To trace allusions in the symbolic art of Egypt to Libra—the

[1] See below, pp. 234, 235.

third in order of the constellations we are now discussing (see Plate XVII.)—is, it must be confessed, not so simple a matter, and it is with some diffidence that I put forward the following suggestion—*i.e.*, that we may perhaps find in the "two feathers," so prominent in Egyptian mythologic imagery, a reference to the two scales of the Balance (Libra).

In allegorical language *we* speak often of the even scales of Justice, and in art the goddess is always represented with the Balance in her hand. In Egyptian symbolism and art, I think the two feathers represented the equal weights of the scales of Justice. In the great judgment hall of Osiris, the souls of men were weighed in the balance. The soul, or heart, of the dead Egyptian was placed in one scale, while a feather—or the figure of the goddess Mait, wearing on her head a single plume or feather—occupied the other. Mait was the goddess of Justice, and we often read also of "the two Maits who preside over Justice and Truth."

The Didû dressed.

There is a woodcut in Prof. Maspero's *Dawn of Civilization*, p. 130, in which the head-dress—the symbolic head-dress—so often to be met with in Egyptian mythologic representations, is very clearly drawn. It was in studying this woodcut that the idea first suggested itself to my mind, that in this head-dress we may find a reference to the four constellations which, when the Zodiac was first imagined, marked the four colures—the four quarters of the heavens—that it was in fact an astronomic monogram, combining four figures in one.

In this head-dress very plainly are to be seen the horns of a ram, and those of a goat. Less convincingly, perhaps, the disc from which spring the goat's horns suggests "the disc enclosing a scarabeus,"[1] under which form the sun as *Khophri*—"He who is"[2]—was sometimes represented by the Egyptians.

The two feathers in outline clearly show themselves, but to connect these two feathers with the scales of Libra is only adventured as a possible means of giving an astronomic value to the so often repeated combination of the forms in this head-dress.

As to Capricornus (the fourth of the constellations which marked the colures 6000 B.C.), (see Plate XVIII.), we do not meet with any representations, so far as I know, of a goat-fish on Egyptian monuments, but on Babylonian boundary stones and engraved gems this monster is often to be seen, exactly represented in form and attitude as on the Grecian sphere. The goat's *horns* are all we find portrayed in ancient Egyptian art, and when they are portrayed they appear together with the *ram's horns*, and often springing out of a ram's head. For this curt reference to the goat (Capricornus) a reason may be found by remembering that this constellation, *in opposition*, presided—traditionally—over the least honoured season of the Egyptian year—the arid season preceding the inundations.

It should be borne in mind that all the Egyptian mythologic symbolism we have been considering must necessarily have only embodied traditions already even under the earliest dynasties extremely ancient; for it was, as may be seen in the Plates, about 6000 B.C. that the colures touched the extreme western degrees of the constellations Aries, Cancer, and Libra—and a point some degrees to the west of Capricornus, as it is now drawn. In each succeeding century the colures moved still more to the west, through the stars, and from 6000 down to 4000 B.C. they were no longer to be observed in the four already named constellations, but in Pisces, Gemini, Virgo, and Sagittarius.

[1] Maspero, p. 139. [2] *Ibid.* p. 138.

It is curious to note that there seems to be no pronounced allusion in Egyptian art or literature to these four constellations, though there are indications (see pp. 230–238) which may lead us to believe that the astronomical phenomena of the later date, 4000 B.C., were closely observed, and seem to have formed the basis of much of the mythology of Egypt.

These facts tend to confirm the conclusion—so often advocated in this book—that the ancestors of the Egyptians, as also of all the great civilized nations of antiquity, followed through many long ages the same sidereal calendar—one based on the observation of the colures amongst the fixed stars 6000 B.C. And it would seem that not till about 4000 B.C., when the colures had traversed, from east to west, the constellations Pisces, Gemini, Virgo, and Sagittarius, and had arrived at the eastern degrees of Aquarius, Taurus, Leo, and Scorpio, did astronomic authorities in Egypt direct their attention to a reform of the calendar and introduce into it, and into religious observances, references to these four last-named constellations.

Turning to Plate XVI. we may notice that the equinoctial colure, marking out as it does the extreme western limits of the constellation Cancer, passes also through a part of the constellation Gemini. This fact may, I think, help to explain some of the legends connected with the twins Castor and Pollux in ancient lore.

A very brilliant star glitters on the head of each twin. These stars are of almost equal lustre and well deserve the name of twin stars; and so we can easily suppose how it was that the imaginative astronomers who, at the early date in question, mapped out the figures of the Zodiac, noticing that the equinoctial colure passed between these two bright stars, should have elected to represent them as marking the heads of twin figures, which they determined should symbolize the *equal day and night* of the season over which they presided.

These two stars, thousands of years after they had ceased to mark the equinox, were still associated by the Greeks with the twin heroes—Castor and Pollux—brothers who, according to the legend, were "possessed of an immortality of existence so divided among them, that as one dies, the other revives." The learned Dr Barrett has pointed out that "this furnishes a complete description of Day and Night." This remark of Dr Barrett's becomes especially interesting if we attribute the first symbolizing of day and night by these stars to the work of astronomers at a date when the day and night these stars symbolized were of exactly equal length, and when, therefore, the equal stars and equal alternation of light and darkness might both be fitly symbolized as twins.

At Plate XVIII. it is to be observed that the equinoctial colure, instead of adjoining Capricornus, occupies an almost central position in the preceding constellation, Sagittarius. This fact, together with other considerations, has led me to think that originally only the bow and arrow of Sagittarius were imagined for that division of the ecliptic; and that the huge composite figure of the archer—half man and half horse—was added to the original design in later ages, by astronomers who chose the spring equinox instead of the winter solstice for the beginning of the year.

In discussing the Median calendar, the importance which seems to have been given by the ancestors of the Medes to the constellation Sagittarius, at a date when it marked the spring equinox, was dwelt upon. It will, I think, appear likely, when we come to study Plates XIX. and XX., that as early as 4600 B.C. constellations were imagined to honour and mark the equinoctial as well as the solstitial seasons.

Perhaps then, at that date the constellation Sagittarius was extended to its present dimensions; and it may be that some centuries later, when the colure of the *winter solstice* had passed into the constellation Aquarius, some astronomers desired—like Gudea of Lagash and Tchuen-Hio in China—to honour that season, and to make it the beginning of the year. It may be that such astronomers dealt with the eleventh constellation of the Zodiac, as earlier ones had dealt with Sagittarius, and that they added to what was possibly originally only a *water jar*, Amphora, the figure of the *water pourer* Aquarius.

These ideas are put forward very speculatively. They were partly suggested by noticing that in the Indian Zodiac the name of the constellation Sagittarius is merely Dhanus (arrow), and the name of Aquarius is Kumbha (water jar).

In the diagrams which we have been discussing, it will be observed that only the twelve figures of the Zodiac, and *two* of the extra-Zodiacal constellations, are given in continuous outline, one of these two is Draco—the dragon or serpent whose folds surround the *Pole of the Ecliptic*—the central point of the circle of the Zodiac.

That the astronomers who traced out the circle of the Zodiac on the heavens, and imagined its twelve strange figures, should also have devoted attention to, and marked out, its central point, is not improbable. The *Pole of the Ecliptic*, unlike the *Pole of the Heavens*, is immoveable amongst the fixed stars. At 6000 B.C., as at the present date, the stars of Draco surrounded this point—a point not itself marked by any conspicuous star. We have not, however, I think, at present sufficient grounds for deciding at what exact date the constellation Draco was imagined under the form it now holds. But that it is very ancient there is no doubt.

For the first depicting on the vault of heaven of the figure of Bootes, I claim with much stronger conviction the date of 6000 B.C., and the latitude of 45° north. For then and there Bootes might be seen at midnight of the summer solstice, standing upright on the northern horizon, his head reaching nearly to the Pole of the Heavens. Never since that date has he held so commanding a position in the sky, nor at any more southern latitude could his whole figure have been represented as standing on the horizon.

One further suggestion as to this constellation I am tempted to make. Not, it is true, on the same firm astronomical grounds as those put forward for the date of the first imagining of the figure, but a suggestion based on the Greek name of the constellation.

The name Bootes has been translated as ox-driver, and of him Aratos says :—

> "The *Bear-ward*, whom mankind the *Ploughman* call,
> Because he seems to touch the wain-like *Bear*." [1]

The seven bright stars which mark the tail and part of the body of the Great Bear are often spoken of as "the Plough," and in the large remaining space allotted on the sphere to the constellation Ursa Major, it would not be difficult to include oxen harnessed to the brightly marked celestial plough.

I have said that at midnight of the summer solstice the constellation Bootes—if we suppose it to have been imagined at 6000 B.C.—presided visibly over the northern sky. But we have learnt from the month names in the Accadian calendar that the astronomers who instituted it always directed attention to the constellations which *invisibly* accompanied the sun in his daily journeyings from east to west, rather than to those which (in opposition) were visible through the hours of the night. For example—all through the mid-winter month of the sacrifice of righteousness, the stars of the Ram—the celestial symbol of that sacrifice—were invisible, hidden in the overpowering light of the sun. In like manner, I think, we may assume that at the close of the Accadian year—in the "month of the sowing of seed" or in "the dark month of sowing," when mortal husbandmen were following on earth their ox-drawn ploughs, Bootes, the ox-driver, though invisible to the bodily eye, appeared to the mental vision of the

[1] *The Phainomena or "Heavenly Display" of Aratos, done into English verse* by Robert Brown, Jun., F.S.A., line 92.

astronomer, following unweariedly the ox-drawn plough in the sky.

The various suppositions here put forward will lead those who accept them as probably correct, to picture to themselves the existence, at the early date of 6000 B.C., in latitude 45° N., of a race of men—not savages, and not merely pastoral nomads—but a race of agriculturists who tilled the ground and reaped its fruits—a race possessed of high intellectual power—who respected law and justice, and whose religion taught them to offer to their god "sacrifices of righteousness."

PLATES XIX. AND XX.

IN Plate XIX., fig. 1, it is the constellation known in the Grecian sphere as Hercules that claims our attention. At the date and latitude above named, this constellation, if then it had already been imagined, culminated gloriously on the northern meridian at midnight of the spring equinox. The head of the hero, or demi-god, touched the very zenith, and with his club brandished aloft he must have seemed well fitted to triumph over, not only the dragon coiled beneath his feet, but over every opposing power.

As was said at p. 223 about Bootes, 6000 B.C., so it may here be repeated of Hercules, 4667 B.C., "never since that date has he held so commanding a position in the sky."

At the present date of writing, and in our English latitudes, Hercules "will ever rise reversed,"[1] and through the summer and autumn months his kneeling figure is always to be seen hanging head downwards in the southern quarter of the sky.

Grecian writers, some centuries B.C., were already puzzled to account for this "*reversed*" position of "the Kneeler." Aratos, from whom I have quoted above, thus further wonders as to this constellation. At line 63 we read :—

> ". . . . like a toiling man, revolves
> A form. Of it can no one clearly speak,
> Nor to what toil he is attached ; but, simply,
> *Kneeler* they call him. Labouring on his knees,
> Like one who sinks he seems ;"

and again at line 614—

> "The *Kneeler* . . . .
> He who is ne'er far distant from the *Lyre*,
> Whoe'er this stranger of the heavenly forms
> May be."[1]

---

[1] *The Phainomena or "Heavenly Display" of Aratos, done into English verse* by Robert Brown, Jun., F.S.A., line 669.

4600 B.C. no such difficult speculations could have presented themselves to the minds of those who, in the joyous springtime of the year, beheld in imagination, night after night, the grand and conquering figure of this god or hero, typifying for them, as we may easily suppose, the ever-increasing triumph at that season of the power of light over darkness.

Plate XIX., fig. 2. It was perhaps at this same date that the cluster of stars "led round in circle"[1] close to the bow of Sagittarius, and exactly marking the equinoctial colure, was figured as a *crown*, and that so depicted, as I have contended at page 76, this constellation suggested the symbolic circle, crown, or wreath which sometimes takes the place of the bow in Assur's hand, and which almost always is present in the hand of Ahura Mazda in Median representations of that figure.

At Plate XX., fig. 1, I have drawn the constellation Hydra as it would have appeared at the date 4667 B.C. At pages 117, 118, the reasons which led me to suppose that this constellation was then first imagined have been given.

At Plate XX., fig. 2, it may be seen how 4667 B.C. the figure of Orion very accurately marked the equinoctial colure, and this fact may incline us to suppose that the giant hunter—so often, according to Grecian legend, in conflict with the powers of high Heaven—was depicted about this date by ancient astronomers to represent the strength of the adverse powers which, at the *autumnal* season in the mythologies of northern nations, appear in combat with, and temporarily triumphant over, the powers of light.

In favour of the high date here claimed for the imagining of Orion's figure under very much the same form as that still depicted on our globes, there are some indications to be observed in the Sanscrit names of the Nakshatra, which contains the stars, $\lambda\ \phi_1\ \phi_2$ Orionis—*i.e.*, the stars marking the head of Orion.

[1] *The Phainomena or "Heavenly Display" of Aratos, done into English verse* by Robert Brown, Jun., F.S.A., line 401.

This Nakshatra is known in Hindu astronomy under two quite different names—viz., Mṛigashirsha and Agrahayani. The Sanscrit word, Mṛigashirsha, means literally "Wild beast's head," and B. G. Tilak, in his work, *The Orion; or, Researches into the Antiquity of the Vedas*, basing his opinion upon many ingenious and recondite arguments, supposes that ancient Indian astronomers gave the name of Mṛigashiras to the stars of Orion, which they imagined portrayed in the sky an "Antelope's head" transfixed by an arrow—the arrow being marked by the three bright stars so well known to us as Orion's Belt.

Mṛiga, there can be no doubt, carries often with it in Sanscrit literature the meaning of "antelope": but Tilak expressly says at p. 97, "Though I have translated the word *Mṛigashiras* by 'Antelope's head,' I do not mean to imply that *Mṛiga* necessarily meant 'an antelope' in the Vedic literature." Again, at p. 151, he says: "The word *Mṛiga* in the Rigveda, means according to Sâyaṇa both a lion and a deer."

Again, as to the other name of the Nakshatra—Agrahayani—it has the meaning of "first-going" (of the sun) understood. In a long dissertation on this name, Tilak contends that it marked an important point in the annual course of the sun, and then further seeks to derive the Greek name Orion from the Sanscrit word, Agrahayani. Of the value of the etymological arguments advanced, I am quite unable to judge, but on astronomic grounds it would not seem an improbable derivation.

But the acceptance of Tilak's contention as to the derivation of the name Orion would make it reasonable to suppose that not only the name but also the configuration of the constellation might, in the astronomy of the Greek and Indian nations, resemble each other; and thus we should be more ready to believe that Mṛigashirsha referred to the lion's head on Orion's arm, and not to an "antelope's head"—a head which, as depicted by Tilak at p. 100, would alone have filled nearly all the space in the heavens occupied in the Grecian sphere by the huge figure of the giant hunter known to us as Orion.

The indications furnished by these two Sanscrit Nakshatra names, if they are followed, must lead us to attribute the imagining and naming of the constellation Orion to a time before that when the ancestors of the Greeks and Indians went their separate ways to the west and to the east, and so will strengthen the claim here made for the depicting of the constellation on the sky as early as 4600 B.C.

It will be noted that in the suggestions here offered concerning Hercules, Corona Australis, Hydra, and Orion, a change in the symbolic methods followed by earlier astronomers, 6000 B.C., must be supposed.

It was to the constellations invisibly *accompanying* the sun that the originators of the Zodiac appear to have directed their attention. But the symbolic figures we have now been studying —there can, it seems to me, be little doubt—were designed to mark *visibly*, and, therefore, in *opposition* to the sun, the various seasons of the year.

A great astronomic activity, a sort of astronomic renaissance, in fact, seems to manifest itself as we study the celestial globe at 4600 B.C., and to this date I would attribute the origin of the astronomic myths of many nations.

PLATE XXI.[1]

In *The Median Calendar and the Constellation Taurus* I have put forward considerations drawn from Median and Assyrian sources, which seemed to me to lead to the conclusion that at about the date 4000 B.C. very close attention was given to the position of the colures amongst the fixed stars, and that at that date very special honour was given by the ancestors of the Medes to the constellation Sagittarius—the constellation which at the spring equinox was in opposition to the sun, and therefore visible all through the night. I need not here reiterate what was there advanced on this point concerning Median and Assyrian symbolism, but rather I now desire to draw attention to the existence in *Egyptian* art and mythologic teaching of what I cannot but think is very constant reference to the position of the colures, as they might have been observed—speaking in round numbers—from 4000 down to 2000 B.C.

It will be seen at Fig. 4 that the equinoctial colure, at the earlier of these dates, touched the confines of the constellation Sagittarius, and might even then, with almost equal right, have been claimed as adjoining those of Scorpio. We can well imagine that the astronomic school which carried out the reformation in method discussed above (pp. 222, 227), which resulted in the imagining of the constellations Hercules and Corona Australis, and in the extension, as I suggested, of the boundaries of Sagittarius—we can well imagine that this school would with reluctance admit the baleful image of Scorpio to take the post of leader of the year, so long held by Sagittarius. But from 4000 B.C. onwards to 2000 B.C. the constellations that did actually mark

[1] The figures in this Plate have been drawn from the globe adjusted to the date, 4128 B.C., Lat. 40° N.

the equinoctial and solstitial colures, were Taurus, Scorpio, Leo, and Aquarius.

Volumes of controversy have been written concerning the astronomic teachings of the ceilings of the temples of Denderah and Edfu, as to the position of the colures amongst the fixed stars, suggested by the arrangement of the figures of the Zodiac in both these temples. The date astronomically referred to in these designs was claimed by some to be about 4000 B.C., but when it was proved that these temples had been restored in Ptolemaic times, and the ceilings probably redecorated then, the high claims put forward for the first imagining of these astronomic designs could no longer with certainty be upheld. A strong reaction in opinion then took place, and it was again and again asserted that the Egyptians were probably not even acquainted with the so-called Grecian twelve-fold division of the ecliptic till after the introduction of European culture into Egypt. To seek for allusions in ancient Egyptian mythology or art to any of the twelve Zodiacal constellations was, therefore, a much discouraged attempt.

But if the testimony of the ceilings of the Denderah and Edfu temples is rendered suspect by their Ptolemaic restoration, the same objection cannot be raised against the evidence borne by the ceiling of an ancient Egyptian building, which has certainly not been restored in Ptolemaic times. In the *Description de l'Égypte*,[1] we find a careful drawing of a "Tableau astronomique au Plafond de l'un des tombeaux des rois." In the central portion on either side of this ceiling a monstrous hippopotamus and crocodile are represented, together with various beings depicted on a much smaller scale. In the drawing here given, of one of these central groups, we find, as it seems to me, very clear refer-

[1] *Description de l'Égypte*, 10 vols., Paris, MDCCCXII.–XXIII., Vol. I., Antiquités, planche 95.

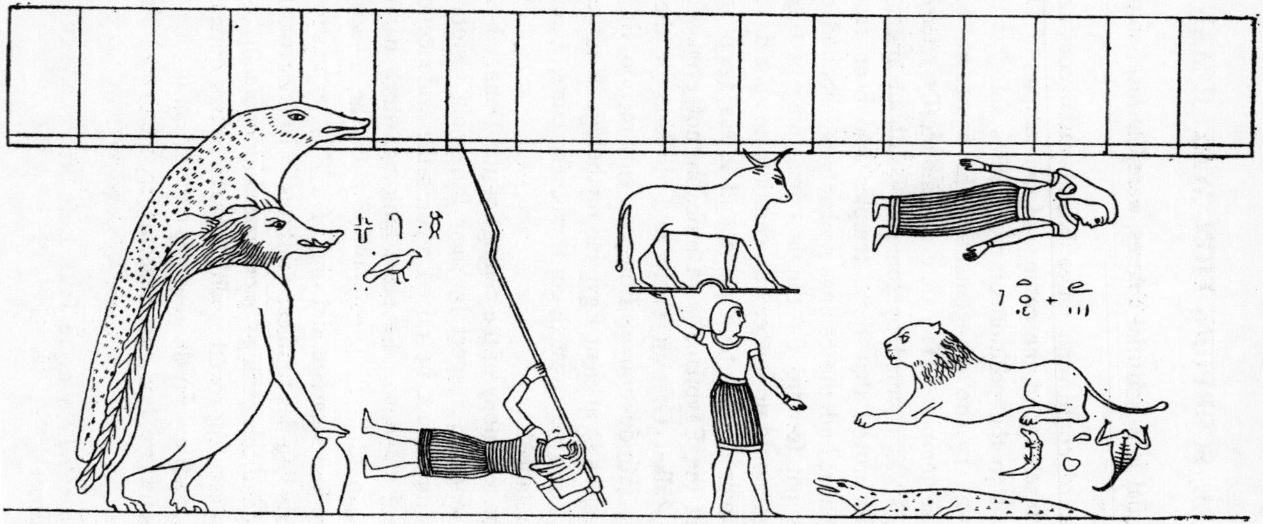

Portion of Ceiling at Bybân-el-Molouk.

[To face p. 233.

ence to the four figures—Taurus, Scorpio, Leo, and Aquarius (=Amphora).

The monstrous hippopotamus and crocodile here depicted are, I am strongly inclined to believe, representations, not of any particular constellation, but rather of the solstitial and equinoctial colures; and the four not at all, except astronomically, related figures of the Bull, Scorpion, Lion, and Water-jar, are here very clearly in evidence.

BULL APIS

In Egyptian mythology the Apis Bull held a very important place. "It was regarded as a symbol and incarnation of Osiris, the husband of Isis, and next to Râ, the great divinity of Egypt." Grecian authorities tell us that the Apis Bull was black, with some distinctive white markings; and on its back (or tongue, according to variant accounts) the figure of a scarabæus was to be observed. From a drawing in Ebers' *Egypt*, Vol. I., p. 121, we may, however, gather, as I think I have seen it elsewhere stated, that the Apis Bull was marked by *equal* areas of black and white. Such equal areas would fitly symbolize the equal day and night of the equinoctial season, and the presence of the scarabæus on the back or tongue of the Bull—if the suggestion made at p. 218 should prove to be correct—would point to the traditional connexion of that creature with the same equinoctial season.

It has often been assumed that the golden calf set up and worshipped in the wilderness by the Israelites was a representation of the Apis god of Egypt; and that so also were the calves set up by Jeroboam in Bethel and in Dan on his return from

Egypt. We read in 1 Kings xii. 32, "And Jeroboam ordained a feast in the eighth month, on the fifteenth day of the month." . . . Ver. 33, "So he offered upon the altar which he had made in Bethel the fifteenth day of the eighth month, even in the month which he had devised of his own heart; and ordained a feast unto the children of Israel: and he offered upon the altar, and burnt incense."

Now, from our knowledge of the Babylonian calendar, and its correspondence with that in use in Palestine, we may conclude that the "eighth month" (Marchesvan), devised by Jeroboam, was that during which the sun traversed the constellation Scorpio, and during which Taurus was dominantly visible all night; and when in this constellation the full moon of the fifteenth or festival day was to be observed. This mention of the *eighth* month in connexion with the worship of the golden calves—a worship, as has been supposed, copied from Egyptian practice—greatly strengthens the opinion that the Apis Bull was in Egypt looked upon as a living representative of the Zodiacal Bull—the constellation which in the time of the early dynasties marked, in opposition to the sun, the autumnal equinox.

In Median mythology and art we have seen the great importance of Tauric symbolism: but there is a wide difference between the Tauric symbolism of the Medes and the Egyptians. Mithras, the Median sun-god, again and again triumphs over and slays the Bull. In Egypt, on the contrary, the Sacred Bull is honoured and worshipped during its lifetime, and reverently embalmed, and with all pomp and glory buried after its death.

This difference in the mythologic conceptions of Media and Egypt may be attributed, I think, to the difference of climatic conditions in the two countries.

In Media, spring—in Egypt, autumn—is the joyous and fruitful season of the year. In the early ages, when Median and Egyptian mythologies took their rise, Taurus was at the spring equinox in conjunction with the sun, and was, therefore, slain by its overwhelming brightness; but at the autumn equinox that same constellation, *in opposition*, rose when the sun set, and all night long was visible. In Median art, it is the Bull immolated by the sun in springtime that is represented. In Egyptian symbolism, it is to the Bull triumphantly traversing the sky by night, in the autumn season, that attention is directed.

In the light of these astronomic considerations, it is interesting to think of the fanatical act of Cambyses in slaying the Apis Bull, as one prompted not only by fury at seeing the high honour paid to the Egyptian god, but also by an insane pride, which made him desire to imitate the triumph of Mithras—the Persian sun-god—over the Bull in the heavens, by killing its earthly representative, the Apis Bull.

In the days of Cambyses, when Apis worship prevailed in Egypt, and even still earlier when the children of Israel, in imitation of this worship, set up the golden calf in the wilderness, the *raison d'être* for the honour paid to Taurus as a star mark of the autumnal season no longer existed; for we know that about 1800 B.C., the equinoctial colure had left that constellation, and had entered the eastern degrees of the constellation Aries. Egyptian history assures us, however, that the institution of the Apis worship was effected by some king of the first dynasty in the far back ages when Taurus, Scorpio, Leo, and Aquarius did actually preside over the four seasons of the year. Moreover, the recent discoveries of the tombs of kings and other personages, in the first Egyptian dynasty, lead us back to the remote date of 4000 B.C., when the very earliest observations of the colures in the four above-named constellations could have been made.

In these ancient tombs, amongst other objects, have been found slate slabs of various shapes—some of them, in their general outline, as it appears to me, representing in the flat the form of a jar or vase. In the accompanying cuts, a proposed restoration of the broken-off top of one of the slates is given, and is distinguished from the existing portion of the slate by being drawn in dotted lines. Both sides of these slabs are covered by finely executed carvings, not incised but in relief. The subjects of the reliefs are very varied, but prominent amongst them, and exactly repeated more than once, is the figure of a bull trampling under his feet, and preparing to gore with his horns, a fallen human foe. Lions are also portrayed in many attitudes, and on one slate, where in the upper register this triumphing bull is represented, below it in a crenellated cartouche a lion and an urn or jar are to be seen in close proximity to each other. On another slate, a scorpion is delineated above a crenellated cartouche; and representations of scorpions carved in relief on mace-heads and on jars, and scorpions carved in the round, have been met with in great numbers in the excavations at Hierakonpolis—the site also of the discovery of one of the most important of the carved slates here described.

It is difficult, I think, to resist the conclusion that we have in the carvings on these ancient slate objects references not to merely terrestrial bulls, lions, scorpions, and water jars, but rather to the constellations, already imagined under those forms, whose stars, at the date when these carvings were made, marked in conjunction with, and in opposition to, the sun, the four seasons of the year.[1]

[1] In the centre of many, if not of all, of the slates under our notice, there is carved on the obverse a ring surrounding a depression. "Mr Quibell's theory, which is still adhered to by Professor Petrie, is that this ring was intended to receive the green paint with which it is supposed the earliest Egyptians painted their faces," but Mr Legge in his Paper, from which I have here quoted (contributed to the *Proceedings of the Society of Biblical Archæology*, May 1900, pp. 137, 138), puts forward a different view, which, if it is correct, would lend support to the astronomic interpretation above proposed for some of the carved representations. Mr Legge considers that the rings

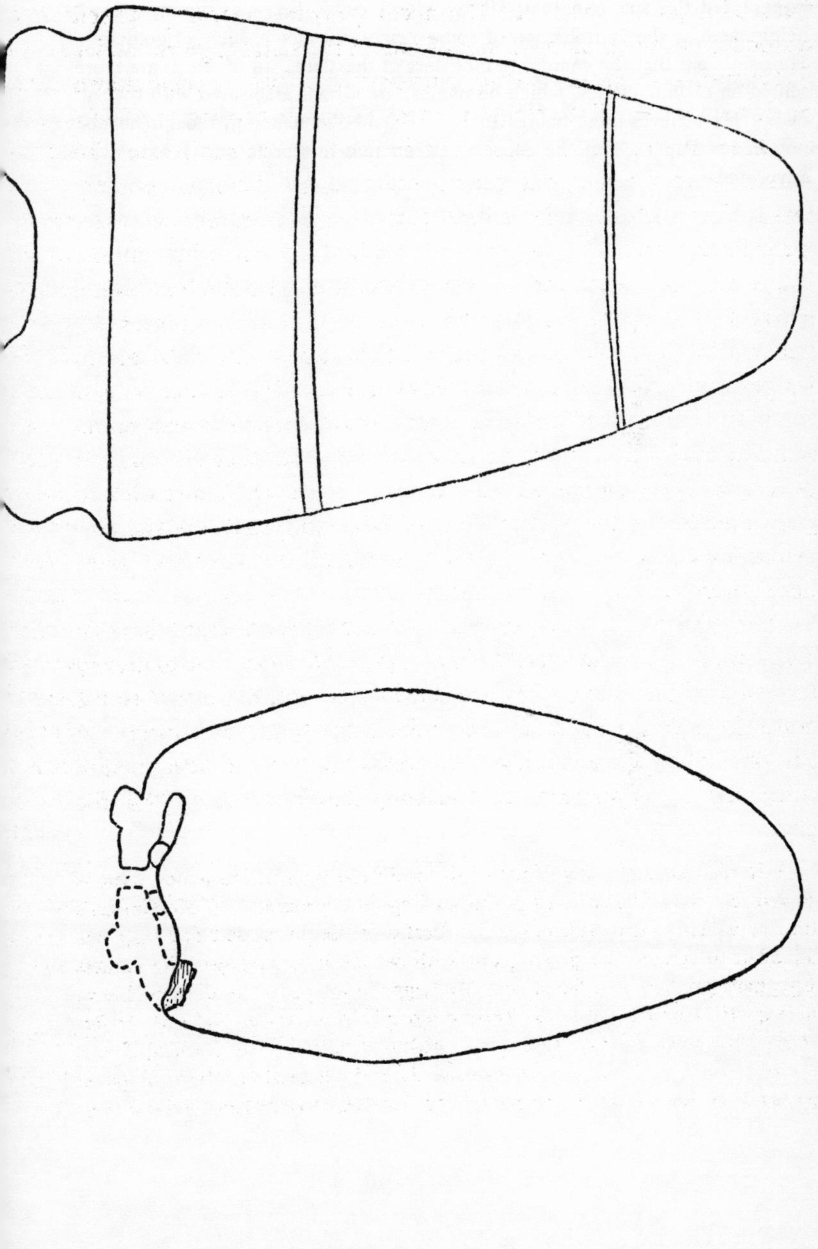

Outlines of two carved slates drawn from Plates I. and III. in *The Proceedings of the Society of Biblical Archæology* for May 1900.

[*To face p.* 236.

represented the sun, and that "it is quite possible that this significance was heightened by the introduction of some bright substance, such as gold foil." He points out that the composite monsters of the slates, all of which are represented on certain ivories, which he names, are always associated with the sun-disk. He believes these figures to have a symbolic meaning, though he does not in his Paper claim the especial astronomic interpretations I have above advocated.

PLATE XXII.[1]

In Grecian legend Cepheus, Cassiopeia, Andromeda, the sea-monster (Cetus), and Perseus are associated together, and on the Grecian sphere five neighbouring constellations represent the actors of the legend.

Studying these constellations as they must have appeared to observers of the heavens at different dates, we shall, I think, see some reason to attribute the imagining of the figure of the hero Perseus to a later age than that of the other members of the group, and, on the other hand, there are considerations which may make us hesitate whether we should not place the origin of the constellation Andromeda at an even earlier date than those of Cepheus, Cassiopeia, and the sea-monster.[2] One point in the legend, however, finds strong astronomic support from a study of the precessional globe—namely, the fact that Cepheus and Cassiopeia were personages of Ethiopian—*i.e.*, of tropical provenance.

It will be seen in Plate XXII., fig. 1, that only in a latitude as far South as 18° N. could the figure of Cassiopeia—even at the early date of 6000 B.C.—have been imagined as that of a queen seated in royal dignity, and visible in the northern quarter of the heavens.

By referring to Plate XV., we may learn that in Lat. 45° N. at that date, Cassiopeia would have appeared in the southern quarter of the sphere, head downwards, while the figure of Cepheus could only have been observed by turning first to one and then to the other quarter of the sky. As, however, the *head of Cepheus* would have marked so exactly the solstitial colure 6000 B.C., it seemed

[1] This plate has been drawn from the globe adjusted to the dates and latitudes of 5744 B.C. Lat. 18° N., and of 3588 B.C., Lat. 23° N.

[2] See below at p. 246, and pp. 242, 243.

to me only right to seek for a latitude in which his figure and that of his queen should appear upright and in the same quarter of the heavens—a latitude, therefore, in which it might be possible to suppose these constellations had been originated as star-marks of the solstitial season. To attain this object it was necessary to set the globe to the very low latitude of 18° N.

To suppose at 6000 B.C. so wide a diffusion, not only of the human race, but also of astronomical science and authority, seemed to involve an historical unlikelihood. Moreover, even if for the sake of suitably establishing the dignity of this regal pair one were tempted to suppose the great improbability of schools of astronomy existing, and with equal authority instituting constellations as star-marks for the year, in regions as far north as Lat. 45° N. and as far south as 18° N.—even so, I do not think the position of the constellations themselves in relation to the solstitial colure as shown in the diagram is by any means so convincingly symmetrical as to force us to accept the date 6000 B.C. for their origin. The head only of Cepheus appears on the meridian, his figure and the whole constellation of Cassiopeia lie considerably to the east of that line.

Under these circumstances it is satisfactory to find at a later, and therefore at a more historically probable date, and still in an Ethiopian (tropical) latitude, a meridian line on and about which the constellations Cepheus, Cassiopeia, Andromeda, and Cetus form a well-balanced group.

This meridian, it is true, is not that of a solstice or an equinox; but it is one which marked a very important astronomical moment —namely, the commencement of the calendrical year—the year counted from the entry of the sun into the constellation Aries. (See Plate XXII., fig. 2.)

Of the high calendrical importance attached through thousands of years to this point in the sun's annual course by the Accadian and Babylonian nations and by the Hindus down to the present day, astronomic records testify. Egyptian mythology and Chinese traditions also, as I have claimed, refer to it: it need not, therefore, surprise us to find constellations imagined to mark the beginning of a year counted from that point, even at a date when this beginning did not coincide either with solstice or equinox.

3500 B.C. is the approximate date I would suggest in a latitude not far from 23° N. for the origin of the constellations Cepheus, Cassiopeia, and probably also for that of Cetus.

The legend tells us that Cassiopeia by boasting of her own or of her daughter's surpassing beauty incurred the enmity of the nereids. She is

> "... that starr'd Ethiop queen that strove
> To set her beauty's praise above
> The sea-nymphs, and their power offended."[1]

It seems to me that for this legend, as for many others, an astronomic basis may be assigned. 3500 B.C. the solstitial colure passed through the constellation Aquarius. The stars of that constellation might then not unfitly have been likened to sea divinities, and rival schools of astronomers and calendar keepers may have exalted the praise, on the one hand, of the stars that marked a calendrical, and, on the other hand, of those that marked a solstitial year.

A curious fact as to the lines in which Aratos refers to the constellation Cassiopeia must here be noted.

Aratos versified "the *Phainomena* of the astronomer Eudoxos, who lived cir. B.C. 403–350." It has often been pointed out that the facts concerning the constellations which Aratos and Eudoxos record "are to a great extent traditional and archaic, and belong to another and far earlier epoch." What is said of Cassiopeia is a case in point; for thus the poet deplores her pride and its punishment at line 654 *et seq.*—

[1] Milton, *Il Penseroso.*

"And now she, too, her daughter's form pursues,
Sad *Kassiepeia*; nor seemly still
Show from her seat her feet and knees above;
But she head foremost like a tumbler sits:
With knees divided: since a doom must fall
On boasts to equal Panopê and Doris." [1]

Now in Eudoxos' time and in his latitude, though Cassiopeia's head did by a few degrees extend into the southern heavens, yet her position was not so deplorably ignominious as the poem would suggest. Three thousand years earlier the pity for her expressed by Aratos would have been more appropriate, for then her whole figure for observers in lat. 35° N. would have been visible in the southern quarter of the sky, and her feet, not her head (as at Lat. 23° N.), would have been on the zenith.

These considerations may lead us to suppose that the idea of Cassiopeia's pride, and the fit punishment of it—*i.e.*, her reversed position in the heavens, must have assumed form in *northern* latitudes almost at as early a date as the constellation figures were first imagined in *tropical* latitudes.

If this be so, it is indeed curious to find a legend which embodied the *animus* of astronomic rivalry 3500 B.C. handed down for thousands of years, and repeated in what professed to be a somewhat scientific treatise at a date between 400 and 300 B.C., when the astronomic facts no longer tallied with those narrated in the legend.

As to Andromeda, the classic story describes her as the daughter of Cepheus and Cassiopeia; but the constellation itself—except on legendary grounds—might equally well have marked the beginning of a solstitial year 6000 B.C., or of a non-solstitial and calendrical year 3500 B.C.

The terrible prevalence of human sacrifices in ancient times, and at the solstices especially, may make us almost fear that the representation of a chained human victim had its place in the sphere at the earlier (solstitial) date.

[1] *The Phainomena or "Heavenly Display" of Aratos, ub. supr.*

The chains which bind Andromeda's arms are fastened by staples to the sky. They appear (at fig. 1) at 6000 B.C. as though driven into two important astronomic lines—*i.e.*, one of them into the line of the equator, the other into that of the solstitial colure. This may, of course, be a mere coincidence, and should not be allowed to weigh at all heavily in the almost evenly adjusted balance of probabilities regarding the date of the origin of the constellation Andromeda. Her story is so interwoven, not only with that of Cepheus and Cassiopeia, but also with that of the sea-monster Cetus, that we should not hastily attempt to dissociate the members of this group.

The very interesting question as to what southern people first depicted the Ethiopic king and queen on the sphere cannot be answered on astronomic grounds. We know that the latitude in which these figures were imagined must have been tropical, if the date of their imagining was as early as 3500 B.C. But we cannot learn from the celestial globe what was the longitude of the land in which they were so imagined. Ethiopia proper, and parts of Arabia and India, lie within the tropics, and the term Ethiopia, in classic writings, embraces all these countries.

Etymologists are, I believe, divided in opinion as to what language the rather un-Grecian names, Cepheus and Cassiopeia, were derived from. Some writers have suggested for their origin the Sanscrit names Capuja and Cassyape: and if, as I have already urged, the Aries-year was followed in ancient Vedic times in India, the Sanscrit derivation suggested will seem not an unlikely one. Nor under these suppositions would it be difficult to propose a possible Sanscrit origin for the name Andromeda, though for this purpose we should have to deprive the legend of all its classic and romantic charm. Cassyape, in Sanscrit story, is not the name of a gloriously beautiful queen, but of a "sage," and it might be that the constellation Andromeda also, for ancient Indian astronomers, represented merely a *human* sacrifice, not that of the beautiful daughter of a beautiful mother. Though in the Rig Veda there is no legend of the sacrifice of a woman, yet in it we meet with seven consecutive hymns referring to the sacrifice, real or symbolical, of Sunahśepas, the son of a rishi or sage, who, according to the commentators, had consented to yield his son up to this cruel fate. The prayers of the victim, addressed to many gods, at last result in his deliverance.

Two other hymns in the Rig Veda relate to the great ceremony of the sacrifice, real or symbolical, of a horse. I give at p. 252 some of the considerations which have convinced me that the praises of the winged steed—*i.e.*, of the constellation Pegasus, and not merely the praises of an earthly horse, are the subject of these two hymns. The ceremony in question bore the name of Aswamedha, literally Horse-Sacrifice.

In reading and comparing these two series of sacrificial hymns, some points of contact present themselves, and, observing this, it occurred to me that some Sanscrit word ending in *Medha* —*i.e.*, sacrifice, and conveying the meaning of *human sacrifice*, might by ancient Indian astronomers have been attached to the constellation, which for us represents the hapless Andromeda: for if we suppose that the constellations Cassiopeia and Cepheus were imagined in India, but adopted with an appropriate legend into the Grecian sphere—the names of the personages in the legend at the same time suffering a Grecian change—it would be easy further to suppose that the Indian name of the constellation near to them, transformed and misunderstood, came to represent in Grecian story not merely a *human* sacrifice, but that of the much-to-be-pitied daughter of the proud Cassiopeia.

Whether these fanciful speculations concerning the names of the actors in the ancient legend be adopted or not need not affect our judgment as to the reasonableness, or otherwise, of the date, 3500 B.C., and of Lat. 23° N. for the origin of the constellational group here discussed.

PLATE XXIII.[1]

THE probable dates for the first imagining of four constellations are here given—namely, for the Centaur, Ophiuchus, Auriga, and Perseus.

For the Centaur the date in round numbers of 3500 B.C. (fig. 1) is suggested: at that date his huge figure would have well marked, in opposition, the beginning of the calendrical Aries-year; or, in conjunction with the sun, the beginning of the seventh month of the same year. It is not necessary, at that date, to attribute a low latitude to the astronomers who designed this figure: in that of 35° N., as shown in the diagram, the whole constellation would then have been well above the horizon. The much earlier epoch of 6000 B.C. might perhaps be claimed for the Centaur. At that date, as I have assumed, the calendrical and the solstitial year coincided. (Compare Plate XVII. and Plate IX.) As between 6000 and 3500 B.C. I have often hesitated, but on the whole I have come to think the later date, as here given, the more probable.

Fig. 2.—Again at the date 3500 B.C. and in the latitude 35° N. I have drawn the constellation Ophiuchus as it would have appeared in opposition to the sun at the season of the spring equinox; triumphing over the powers of darkness—namely, the scorpion on which he treads and the serpent which he crushes with his hands. Although at the date in question Hercules' position in the northern heavens was not quite so commanding and symmetrical as it was a thousand years earlier (see Plate XIX.), yet in the lower latitude given here (Plate XXIII., fig. 2) the heads of

[1] The figures in this plate have been drawn from the globe adjusted to the following dates and latitudes. Figs. 1 and 2, 3589 B.C., Lat. 35° N. Fig. 3, 3050 B.C., Lat. 35° N. Fig. 4, 1443 B.C., Lat. 40° N.

Hercules and of Ophiuchus would have been on the zenith, and these brothers might have been seen, one of them in the northern and the other in the southern quarter of the sky, strongly combating and conquering the forces of winter and darkness at the season of the spring equinox.

Fig. 3.—For Auriga, I have suggested the later date of 3000 B.C., for then the bright star Capella, the most important star in the constellation and one of the brightest in that part of the sky, was on the meridian in conjunction with the sun at noon of the spring equinox—and in opposition at mid-night of the autumn equinox.

The star Capella has, by several writers, been identified with the star "Icu of Babylon" mentioned in many of the Babylonian astrological texts. If this identification of Capella and "Icu of Babylon" should be established as correct, we ought, I suppose, to credit *Babylonian* astronomers with the delineation of the figure Auriga.

Fig. 4.—Unless we adopt on the authority of the Cepheus, Cassiopeia, and Andromeda legend the date 3500 for Perseus, it will seem, I think, almost necessary to attribute the much later one of 1433 B.C. for the designing of this constellation. At the earlier date the position of Perseus—see Plate XXII., fig. 2—militates against the likelihood of its having then been imagined; as part of the figure of Perseus would have been visible in the northern and part in the southern hemisphere.

In favour of the later date we may note the way in which the figure of Perseus has been fitted in, as it were, between already-named constellations, so that though restricted to a small space it still retains heroic proportions.

The star Algol, whose strange alternations of magnitude may well have suggested to the ancients the *winking* of the eye of some malignant monster, was imagined by the astronomers who drew the figure of Perseus, as on the brow of the Gorgon Medusa. It will be seen in the Plate how, at the date there given, this mysterious star exactly marked the equinoctial meridian.

The northern latitude 40° N., suitable for the imagining of this constellation, and its name Perseus, seem to point to an Iranian school of astronomers as the probable originators of this figure.

PLATE XXIV.

It will be seen that by consulting the precessional globe it has been possible to suggest dates at which the various simple and composite human figures, represented on the (Grecian) sphere could have been originally imagined in an upright position, either on the northern or southern meridian at some well-marked time of the year—that is of either a cosmical or a calendrical year.

That many other of the remaining ancient constellations—Canis Major and Canis Minor, Aquila, Cygnus, &c., were depicted and named at very remote dates, there can, I think, be little doubt. The wide-spread traditions connected with these figures demand an early origin for them. It is probable that the *heliacal rising* of certain bright stars in these constellations at some special season of the year, rather than their *culmination at noon or at midnight*, may have been the occasion for the interest taken in them.

A further study of the precessional globe with this thought present would probably suggest approximate dates for the imagining of some of these constellations, small in extent but marked by bright stars.

I will now only allude to the two remaining ancient constellations of *wide extent*—namely, to Argo and Pegasus.

Glancing at Plate X. (Astronomy in the Rig Veda) the almost upright and symmetrical position of Argo 3000 B.C. may suggest the likelihood that at that date or perhaps a few hundred years later, and in a latitude about 12° higher than that given in the diagram, this constellation was imagined. It will be observed that all the stars of Argo, even the bright and southern Canopus at 35° N. would have been above the horizon and visible at midnight of the winter solstice. At noon of the summer solstice they would have been above the horizon, but invisible in conjunction with the sun.

But now turning our thoughts to the constellation Pegasus, a difficulty confronts us at every date from 6000 B.C. downwards even to this present A.D. 1903: Pegasus as depicted on the globe has held and still holds a reversed position in the heavens. The very fact that for all the other ancient constellations which represent living beings, it has been possible to find some season and some date at which they could have been observed upright in the sky, makes it a more imperative need to seek for some explanation of the anomalous treatment meted out by astronomers of old to the winged steed.

In this stress of difficulty, I venture to make a suggestion which will, I fear, at first sight, appear far-fetched and fanciful, and quite out of line with other suppositions put forward in this book.

My suggestion is that an error concerning the right depicting of this constellation was fallen into by some astronomers of old, and that this error was handed down to us through the Grecian school.

If on some clear autumnal or winter night we search for the constellation Pegasus, not on a globe or map but in the southern quarter of the actual sky, we may quickly recognise it by four very bright stars which mark the corners of an almost exact and very extensive *square* on the vault of heaven. Then stretching away from the lower and western corner of this square still farther towards the horizon and to the west, we may trace the faint stars which mark the neck, and the somewhat brighter star which marks the head of the Demi-Horse: while starting from the upper western corner of the square and stretching still higher towards the zenith, and to the west we detect the lines of fainter stars which mark the fore legs and the hoofs of Pegasus. If we allow the four stars of the "square of Pegasus" still to mark the body of the horse, and think of the upper lines of faint stars as marking its neck and head and of the lower ones as marking its fore legs and hoofs, the figure exactly reversed will still fit within the limiting lines of the constellation, with the satisfactory result that the winged steed, not miserably floundering on its back but upright and alert, will be seen in our mental vision night after night pursuing its course from east to west across the heavens.

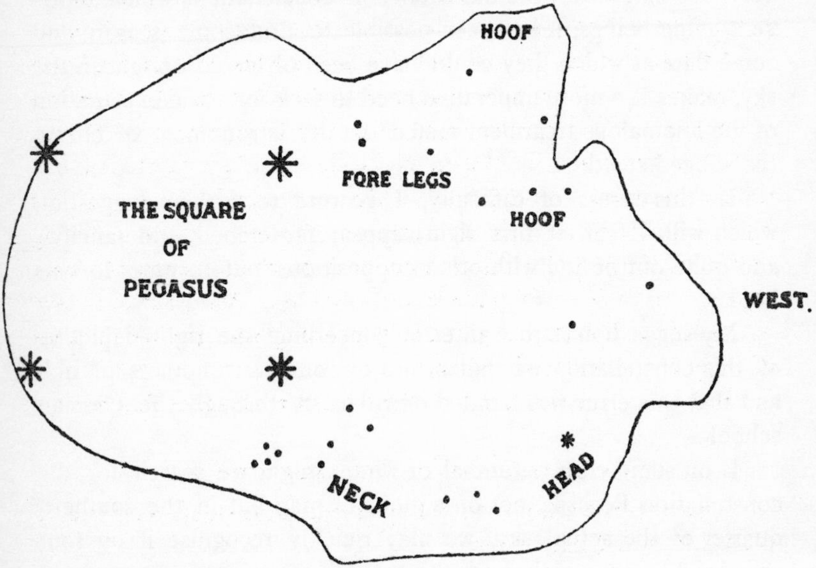

AQUARIUS

But even to arrive at so satisfactory a result, we might scarcely dare to propose without some other plea than its mere desirability, so arbitrary a method of dealing with the reversed position of Pegasus, as that of thus correcting a supposed error on the part of early astronomers.

There is, however, I think, in Grecian and in Vedic legend some support to be found for the opinion that the original position of Pegasus was upright and not reversed.

Though on the Grecian astronomic sphere Pegasus appears reversed, on no artistic monument, vase, or coin is he thus represented, and in Grecian legend he is ever a glorious and highly-prized friend and helper of gods and heroes. Amongst other achievements, we read of him that he produced with a blow of his hoof the inspiring fountain Hippocrene.

In the Rig Veda we read of a swift horse, belonging to the Aswins, who from his hoof filled a hundred vases of sweet liquor.

Max Müller has pointed out that the Aswins possessed a horse called Pagas. The stars α and β Arietis are in Hindu astronomy called the "Aswins," and at p. 137 I have contended that these stars in Vedic times symbolised the twin heroes, the Aswins, the possessors, according to Max Müller, of the horse Pagas. If we look at Pegasus in the sky, and observe how closely following that constellation the bright stars that mark the head of Aries appear, we shall easily understand how these Aswins might have by Vedic bards been imagined as possessing and driving in front of them the swift steed Pegasus.

In two hymns addressed to the Aswins we read as follows :[1]—

MANDALA I.—Súkta cxvi. and verse 7.

"You filled from the hoof of your vigorous steed, as if from a cask, a hundred jars of wine."

And again in the next hymn, cxvii. verse 6—

"You filled for the (expectant) man a hundred vases of sweet (liquors) from the hoof of your fleet horse."

As Pegasus is now represented his hoofs touch no well or fountain, cask or vase. But if we depict him as suggested above (see Plate XXIV.), his hoof would indeed appear as almost in the act of striking the vase in the constellation Aquarius, from which the abundant waters gush forth.

[1] Wilson's translation of the Rig Veda.

I have already alluded to the Aswamedha hymns in the Rig Veda as probably referring not merely to the sacrifice of an actual horse, but rather to a symbolic sacrifice of the winged horse of the constellation Pegasus. In support of this opinion I will quote from the hymns in question :—

MANDALA I.—Súkta clxii.

" 1. Let neither MITRA nor VARUŃA, ARYAMAN, ÁYU, INDRA, RIBHUKSHIN, nor the *Maruts* censure us : when we proclaim in the sacrifice the virtues of the swift horse sprung from the gods.

" 2. When they, (the priests), bring the prepared offering to the presence (of the horse), who has been bathed and decorated with rich (trappings), the various-coloured goat going before him, bleating, becomes an acceptable offering to INDRA and PÚSHAN.

" 3. This goat, the portion of PÚSHAN, fit for all the gods, is brought first with the fleet courser, so that TWASHT́RI may prepare him along with the horse, as an acceptable preliminary offering for the (sacrificial) food."

Looking at Plate XXIV., Figs. 1, 2, we may observe how the constellation Capricornus "goes before" that of Pegasus, and we may understand the aspiration that Twasht́ri may prepare him along with the horse as an acceptable preliminary offering.

After many verses entering into minute and rather horrible details of the "immolation" and even of the cooking of the sacrificial horse the 19th verse adds—

"There is one immolator of the radiant horse, which is Time"; and these words seem to carry us back from thoughts of an actual to a, in some way, symbolical sacrifice, especially when at verse 21 we read;

"Verily at this moment thou dost not die; nor art thou harmed; for thou goest by auspicious paths to the gods. The horses of INDRA, the steeds of the *Maruts* shall be yoked (to their cars), and a courser shall be placed in the shaft of the ass of the AŚWINS (to bear thee to heaven)."

The following hymn (lxiii.) I give *in extenso*:—

MANDALA I.—Súkta clxiii.

1. Thy great birth, O Horse, is to be glorified; whether first springing from the firmament or from the water, inasmuch as thou hast neighed (auspiciously), for thou hast the wings of the falcon and the limbs of the deer.

2. TRITA harnessed the horse which was given by YAMA: INDRA first mounted him, and GANDHARBA seized his reins. *Vasus*, you fabricated the horse from the sun.

3. Thou, horse, art YAMA: thou art A'DITYA: thou art TRITA by a mysterious act: thou art associated with SOMA. The sages have said there are three bindings of thee in heaven.

4. They have said that three are thy bindings in heaven; three upon earth; and three in the firmament. Thou declarest to me, Horse, who art (one with) VARUÑA, that which they have called thy most excellent birth.

5. I have beheld, Horse, these thy purifying (regions); these impressions of the feet of thee, who sharest in the sacrifice; and here thy auspicious reins, which are the protectors of the rite that preserve it.

6. I recognise in my mind thy form afar off, going from (the earth) below, by way of heaven, to the sun. I behold thy head soaring aloft, and mounting quickly by unobstructed paths, unsullied by dust.

7. I behold thy most excellent form coming eagerly to (receive) thy food in thy (holy) place of earth; when thy attend-

ant brings thee nigh to the enjoyment (of the provender), therefore greedy, thou devourest the fodder.

8. The car follows thee, O Horse: men attend thee; cattle follow thee; the loveliness of maidens (waits) upon thee; troops of demi-gods following thee have sought thy friendship; the gods themselves have been admirers of thy vigour.

9. His mane is of gold; his feet are of iron; and fleet as thought, INDRA is his inferior (in speed). The gods have come to partake of his (being offered as) oblation; the first who mounted the horse was INDRA.

10. The full-haunched, slender-waisted, high-spirited, and celestial coursers (of the sun), gallop along like swans in rows, when the horses spread along the heavenly path.

11. Thy body, horse, is made for motion; thy mind is rapid (in intention) as the wind; the hairs (of thy mane) are tossed in manifold directions; and spread beautiful in the forests.

12. The swift horse approaches the place of immolation, meditating with mind intent upon the gods; the goat bound to him is led before him; after him follow the priests and the singers.

13. The horse proceeds to that assembly which is most excellent: to the presence of his father and his mother (heaven and earth). Go, (Horse), to-day rejoicing to the gods, that (the sacrifice) may yield blessings to the donor.

Many passages in this hymn, such as those in verse 3 referring to Trita and Soma, may suggest corroborative astronomic observations,[1] but I would here especially refer to the description, verse 1, of the horse possessing "the wings of the falcon," and in verse 6 to the words, "I behold *thy head soaring aloft*, and mounting quickly by unobstructed paths, unsullied by dust."

As I read these hymns I cannot think merely of an actual

[1] V. pp. 176, 177.

horse led to sacrifice, but of the winged celestial Pegasus; nor is it easy to think of that celestial horse as it is at present depicted, *reversed* in the sky.

The Vedic poet beheld his head soaring aloft, but in the previous verse he has said, "I have beheld Horse, . . . those impressions of the feet of thee"; and if these "impressions" were the stars which, on the Grecian sphere, marked the horse's head, but, as I have contended, originally marked his hoof, then we shall understand how, associated with Soma, and identical with Trita by a mysterious act—*i.e.*, at the season of the summer solstice, and when the moon was at its full in the constellation Aquarius, ancient astronomers imagined to themselves the horse Pegasus producing with his hoof the sweet exhilarating waters of the fountain Hippocrene.

The date of this particular legend concerning the hoof of Pegasus I should be inclined to place at about 3000 B.C., when the solstitial colure was so closely marked by "those impressions of the feet" of the "swift horse sprung from the gods." For the first imagining of the constellation I think that of 4000 B.C. is more probable (see Plate XXIV., Figs. 1, 2).

PLATE XV.

5,744 B.C.　　　　Lat. 45° N.

Constellations above Southern Horizon.
Invisible—Noon, Winter Solstice.
Visible—Midnight, Summer Solstice.

FIG. 2.

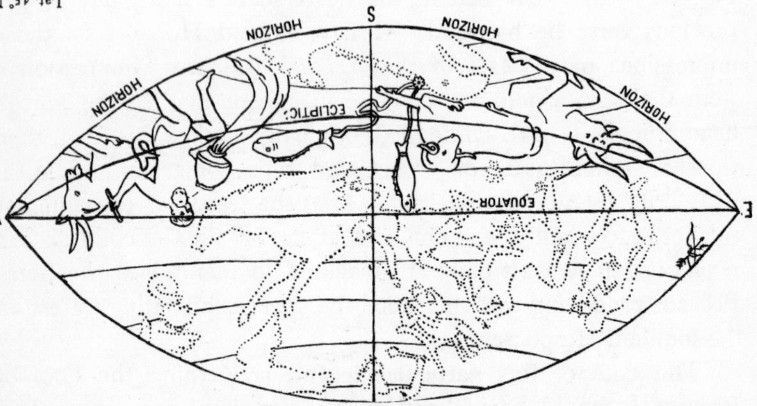

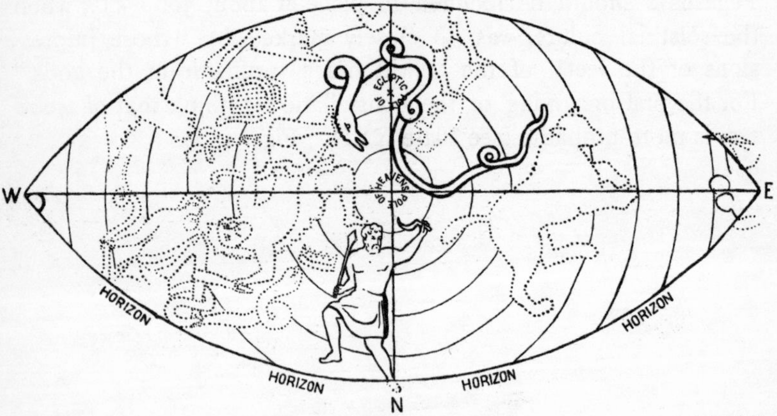

5,744 B.C.　　　　Lat. 45° N,

Constellations above Northern Horizon.
Invisible—Noon, Winter Solstice.
Visible—Midnight, Summer Solstice,

FIG. 1.

PLATE XVI.

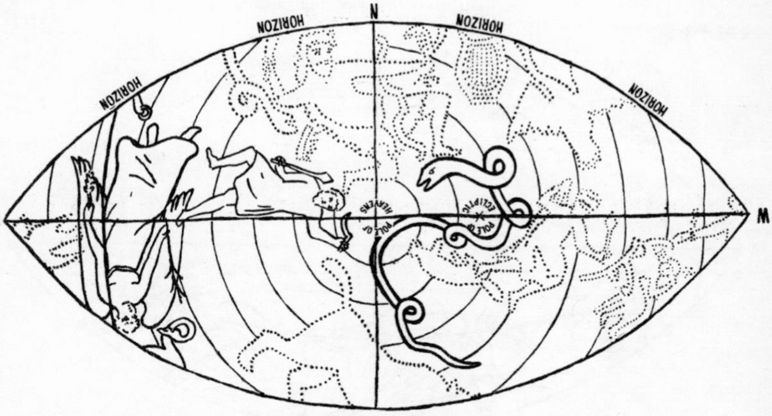

5,744 B.C.

Lat. 45° N.

Constellations above Northern Horizon.
Invisible—Noon, Spring Equinox.
Visible—Midnight, Autumn Equinox.

FIG. 1.

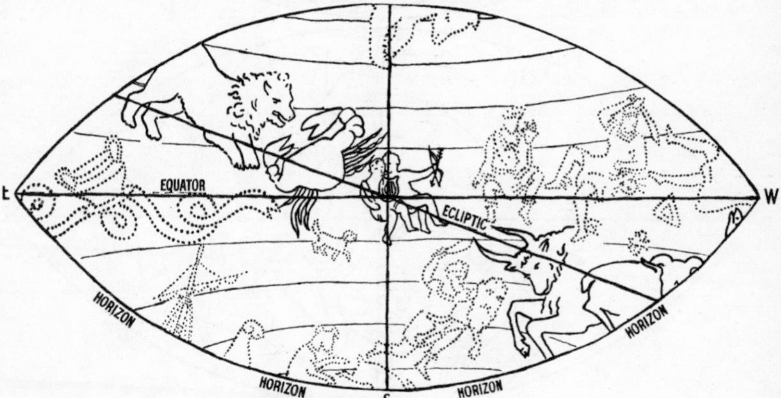

5,744 B.C.

Lat. 45° N.

Constellations above Southern Horizon.
Invisible—Noon, Spring Equinox.
Visible—Midnight, Autumn Equinox.

FIG. 2.

PLATE XVII.

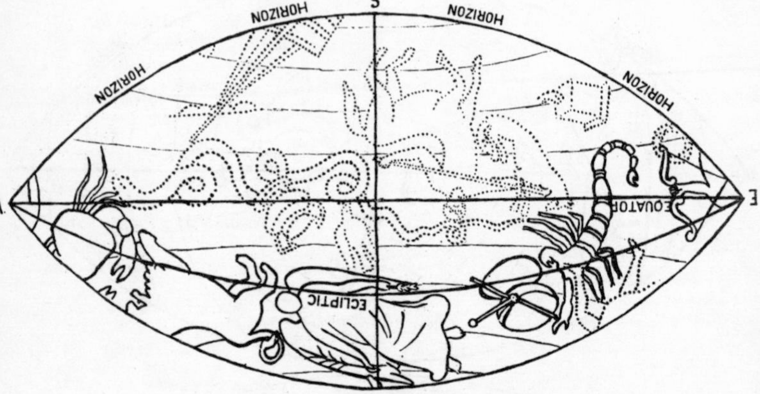

5,744 B.C.

Lat. 45° N.

Constellations above Southern Horizon.
Invisible—Noon, Summer Solstice.
Visible—Midnight, Winter Solstice.

FIG. 2.

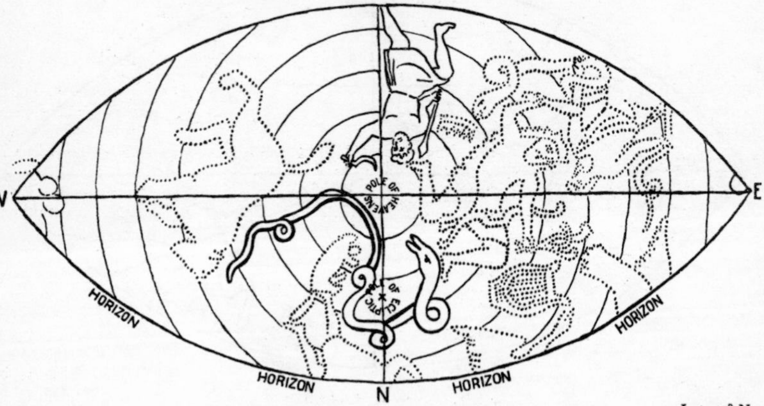

5,744 B.C.

Lat. 45° N.

Constellations above Northern Horizon.
Invisible—Noon, Summer Solstice.
Visible– Midnight, Winter Solstice.

FIG. 1.

PLATE XVIII.

5,744 B.C. Lat. 45° N.

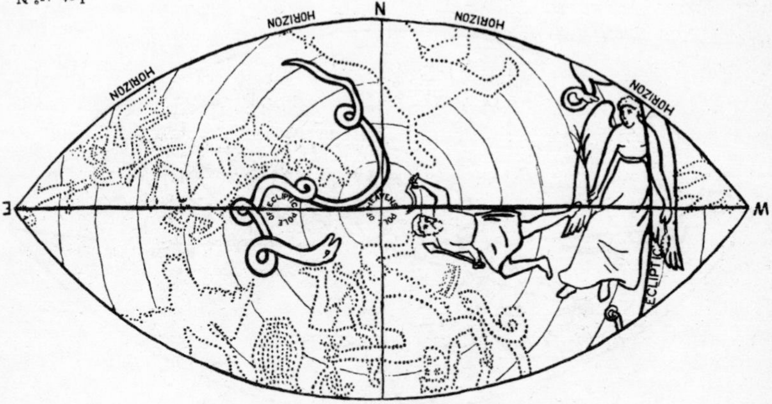

Constellations above Northern Horizon.
Invisible—Noon, Autumn Equinox.
Visible—Midnight, Spring Equinox.

FIG. 1.

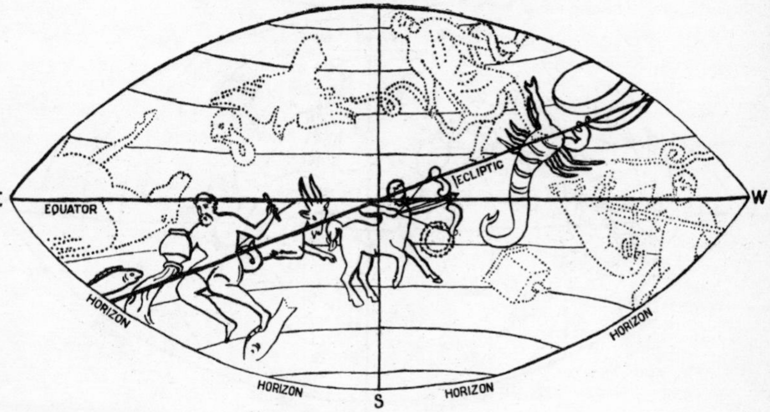

5,744 B.C. Lat. 45° N.

Constellations above Southern Horizon.
Invisible—Noon, Autumn Equinox.
Visible—Midnight, Spring Equinox.

FIG. 2.

PLATE XIX.

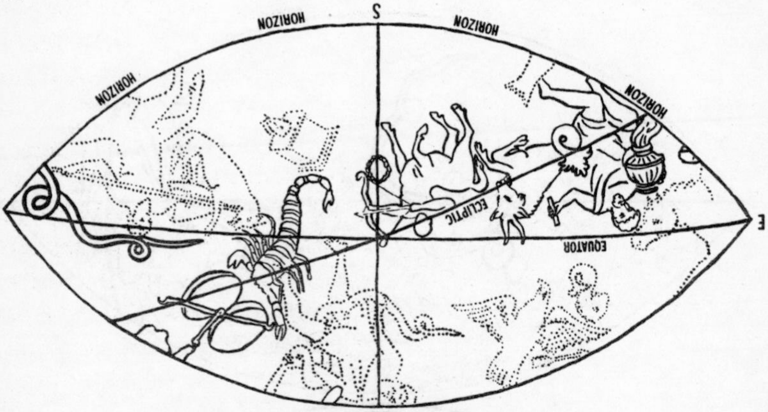

4,667 B.C.

Lat. 40° N.

Constellations above Southern Horizon.
Invisible—Noon, Autumn Equinox.
Visible—Midnight, Spring Equinox.

FIG. 2.

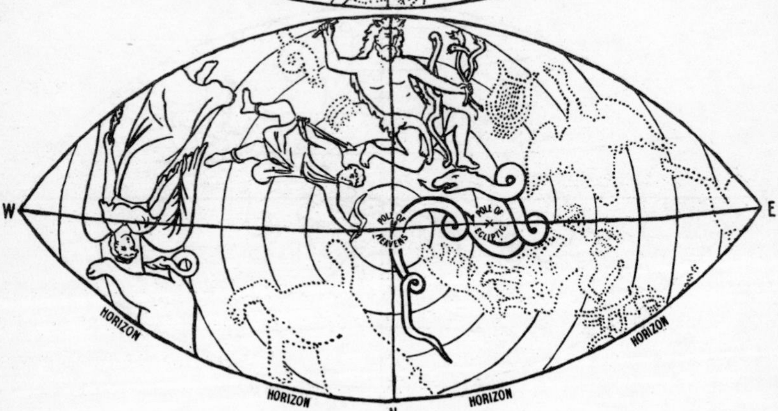

4,667 B.C.

Lat. 40° N.

Constellations above Northern Horizon.
Invisible—Noon, Autumn Equinox.
Visible—Midnight, Spring Equinox.

FIG. 1.

PLATE XX.

4,667 B.C. Lat. 40° N.

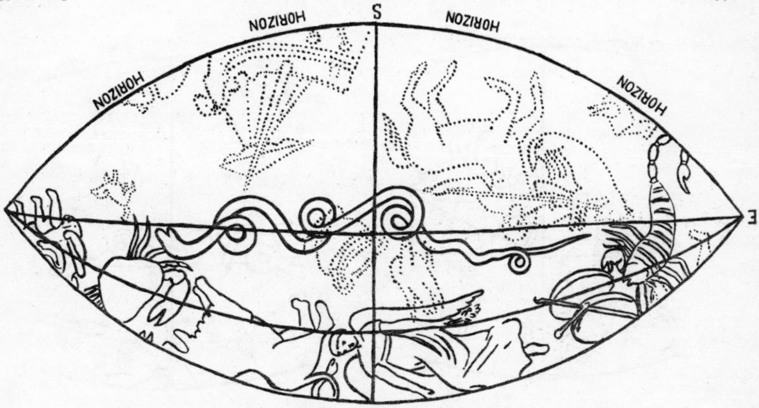

Constellations above Southern Horizon.
Invisible—Noon, Summer Solstice.
Visible—Midnight, Winter Solstice.

FIG. 1.

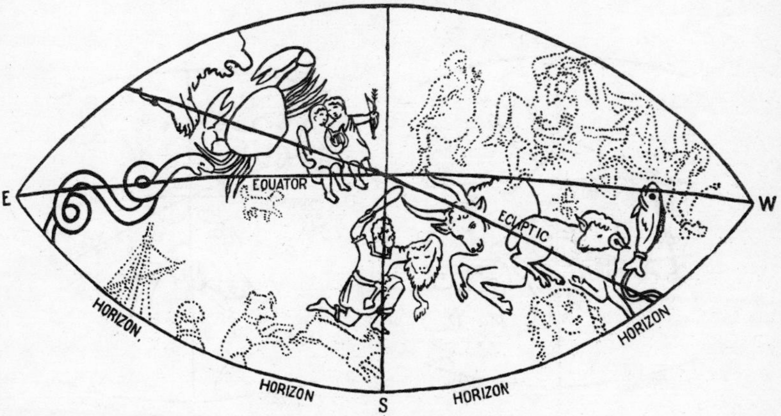

4,667 B.C. Lat. 40° N.

Constellations above Southern Horizon.
Invisible—Noon, Spring Equinox.
Visible--Midnight, Autumn Equinox.

FIG. 2.

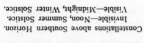

PLATE XXI.

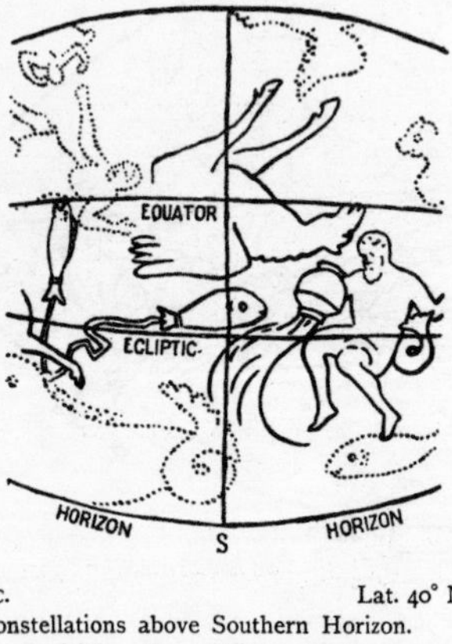

4,128 B.C. Lat. 40° N.

Constellations above Southern Horizon.
Invisible—Noon, Winter Solstice.
Visible—Midnight, Summer Solstice.

FIG. 1.

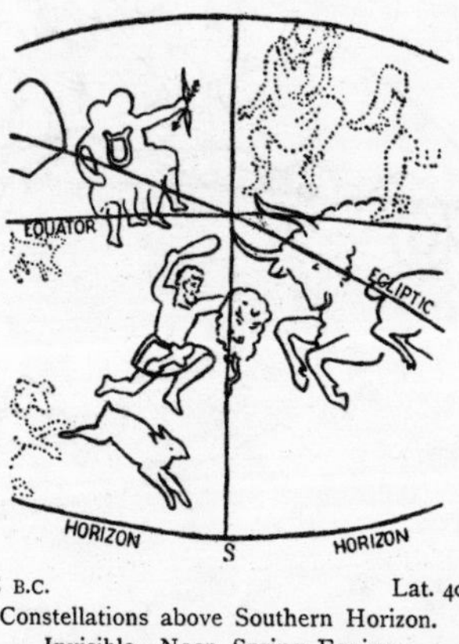

4,128 B.C. Lat. 40° N.

Constellations above Southern Horizon.
Invisible—Noon, Spring Equinox.
Visible—Midnight, Autumn Equinox.

FIG. 2.

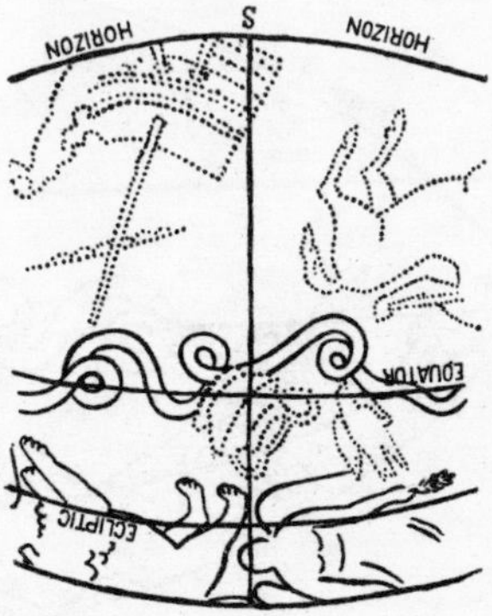

4,128 B.C. Lat. 40° N.

Constellations above Southern Horizon.
Invisible—Noon, Summer Solstice.
Visible—Midnight, Winter Solstice.

FIG. 3.

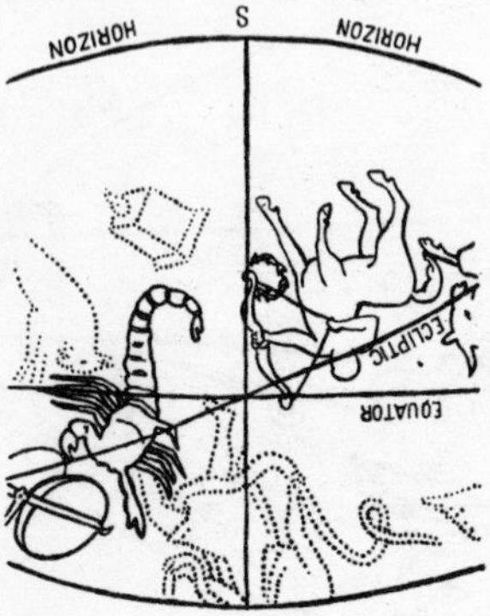

4,128 B.C. Lat. 40° N.

Constellations above Southern Horizon.
Invisible—Noon, Autumn Equinox.
Visible—Midnight, Spring Equinox.

FIG. 4.

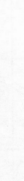

PLATE XXII.

5,744 B.C. Lat. 18° N.
Constellations above Northern Horizon.
Invisible—Noon, Winter Solstice.
Visible—Midnight, Summer Solstice.

FIG. 1.

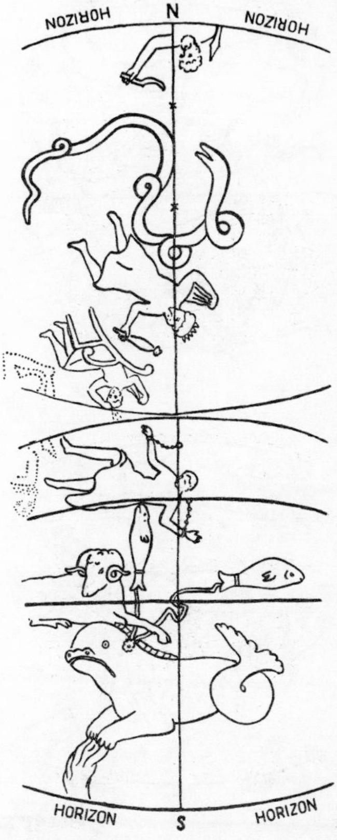

5,744 B.C. Lat. 18° N.
Constellations above Southern Horizon.
Invisible—Noon, Winter Solstice.
Visible—Midnight, Summer Solstice.

FIG. 2.

3,589 B.C. Lat. 23° N.
Constellations above Northern Horizon.
Invisible—Noon beginning Calendrical Year.
Visible—Midnight, 7th Month, Calendrical Year.

FIG. 3.

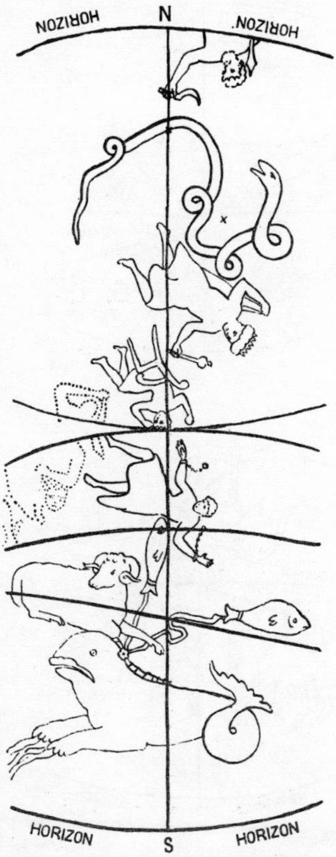

3,589 B.C. Lat. 23° N.
Constellations above Southern Horizon.
Invisible—Noon, beginning Calendrical Year.
Visible—Midnight, 7th Month, Calendrical Year.

FIG. 4.

PLATE XXIII.

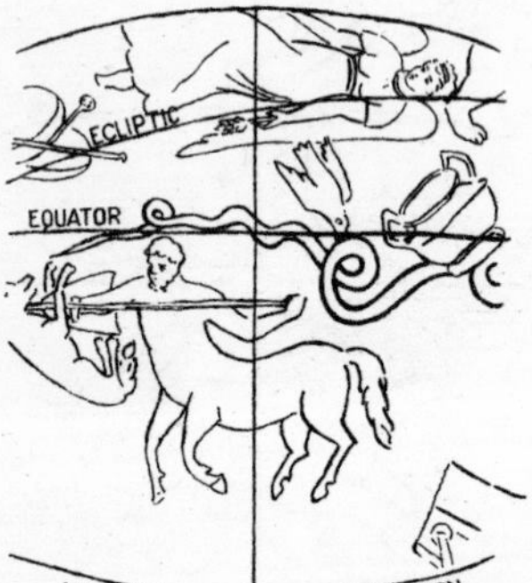

3,589 B.C. Lat. 35° N.

Constellations above Southern Horizon.

Invisible—Noon, 7th Month, Calendrical Year.

Visible—Midnight, beginning Calendrical Year.

FIG. 1.

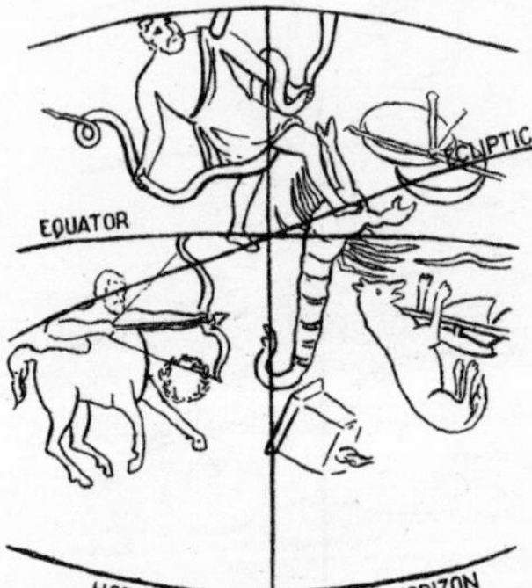

3,589 B.C. Lat. 35° N.

Constellations above Southern Horizon.

Invisible—Noon, Autumn Equinox.

Visible—Midnight, Spring Equinox.

FIG. 2.

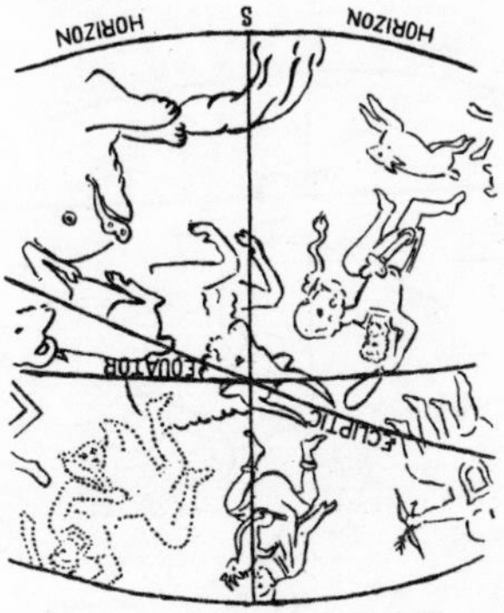

3,050 B.C. Lat. 35° N.

Constellations above Southern Horizon.

Invisible—Noon, Spring Equinox.

Visible—Midnight, Autumn Equinox.

FIG. 3.

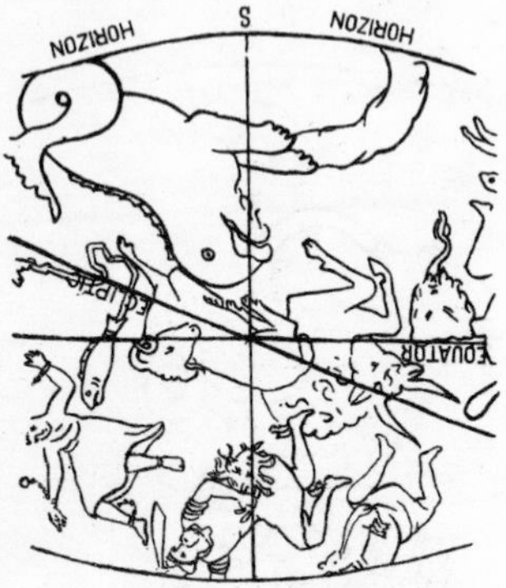

1,433 B.C. Lat. 40° N.

Constellations above Southern Horizon.

Invisible—Noon, Spring Equinox.

Visible—Midnight, Autumn Equinox.

FIG. 4.

PLATE XXIV.

4,128 B.C.

Lat. 40° N.

Constellations above Southern Horizon.
Invisible—Noon, Winter Solstice.
Visible—Midnight, Summer Solstice.

FIG. 1.

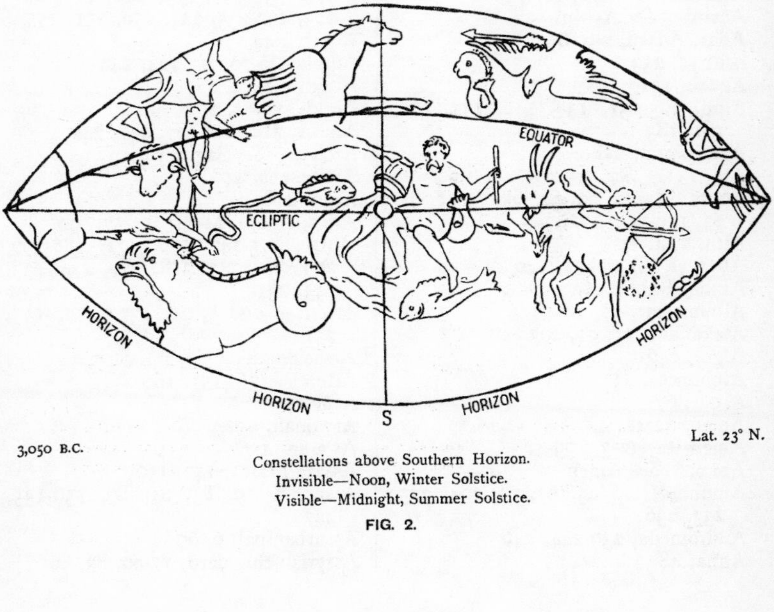

3,050 B.C.

Lat. 23° N.

Constellations above Southern Horizon.
Invisible—Noon, Winter Solstice.
Visible—Midnight, Summer Solstice.

FIG. 2.

INDEX

INDEX

INDEX

INDEX

INDEX

INDEX

INDEX